CW00765974

A sketch of Waterloo Mill from Upbrooks by J Henson Bamford

Cover: The Rover-designed W2B/26 straight-flow engine.

Title Page: Viking Warrior – Rover advertisement of the 1920s

ROLLS-ROYCE HERITAGE TRUST

VIKINGS AT WATERLOO

– The wartime work on the Whittle jet engine by the Rover Company

David S Brooks

HISTORICAL SERIES No 22

Published in 1997 by the
Rolls-Royce Heritage Trust
P O Box 31 Derby England

ISBN: 1 872922 08 2

The Historical Series is published as a joint initiative by the Rolls-Royce Heritage Trust and The Sir Henry Royce Memorial Foundation.

Also published in the series:

No.1 Rolls-Royce – the formative years 1906-1939
Alec Harvey-Bailey RRHT 2nd edition 1983
No.2 The Merlin in perspective – the combat years
Alec Harvey-Bailey, RRHT 4th edition 1995
No.3 Rolls-Royce – the pursuit of excellence
Alec Harvey-Bailey and Mike Evans, HRMF 1984
No.4 In the beginning – the Manchester origins of Rolls-Royce
Mike Evans, RRHT 1984
No.5 Rolls-Royce – the Derby Bentleys
Alec Harvey-Bailey, HRMF 1985
No.6 The early days of Rolls-Royce – and the Montagu family
Lord Montagu of Beaulieu, RRHT 1986
No.7 Rolls-Royce – Hives, the quiet tiger
Alec Harvey-Bailey, HRMF 1985
No.8 Rolls-Royce – Twenty to Wraith
Alec Harvey-Bailey,HRMF 1986
No.9 Rolls-Royce and the Mustang
David Birch, RRHT 1987
No.10 From Gipsy to Gem with diversions, 1926-1986
Peter Stokes, RRHT 1987
No.11 Armstrong Siddeley – the Parkside story, 1896-1939
Ray Cook, RRHT 1989
No.12 Henry Royce – mechanic
Donald Bastow, RRHT 1989
No.14 Rolls-Royce – the sons of Martha
Alec Harvey-Bailey, HRMF 1989
No.15 Olympus – the first forty years
Alan Baxter, RRHT 1990
No.16 Rolls-Royce piston aero engines – a designer remembers
A A Rubbra, RRHT 1990
No.17 Charlie Rolls – pioneer aviator
Gordon Bruce, RRHT 1990
No.18 The Rolls-Royce Dart – pioneering turboprop
Roy Heathcote, RRHT 1992
No.19 The Merlin 100 series – the ultimate military development
Alec Harvey-Bailey and Dave Piggott, RRHT 1993
No.20 Rolls-Royce – Hives' turbulent barons
Alec Harvey-Bailey, HRMF 1992
No.21 Rolls-Royce – The Crecy Engine
Nahum, Foster-Pegg, Birch, RRHT 1994

Books are available from:
Rolls-Royce Heritage Trust, Rolls-Royce plc, Moor Lane, PO Box 31, Derby DE24 8BJ

Origination and Reproduction by Neartone Ltd, Arnold, Nottingham
Printed by Premier Print, Glaisdale Parkway, Bilborough, Nottingham

CONTENTS

FOREWORD

The place of Clitheroe and Barnoldswick in the story of the evolution of the jet engine has long been recognised, but the achievements had largely gone unrecorded until the publication of Sir Stanley Hooker's "Not Much Of An Engineer". Even then his story majors on his personal involvement when Rolls-Royce took over the 'Northern Factories' from Rover in 1943. It remained a fact that very little had been written specially to record the early significant achievements of Rover and Lucas with Frank Whittle's W2B jet engine, nor of the development of Rover's B26 'straight-flow' engine. Thus, there was seen to be a need for a more detailed account of the period up to the point at which the famous swap took place, between Rover and Rolls-Royce, of the former's jet engine work for the latter's production of Meteor tank engines.

David Brooks formerly worked with A V Roe & Co Ltd, but in more recent times, as a retired teacher with life-long interests in aviation and local history, he decided to address these omissions by producing a manuscript which could be used as a reference source for local studies. The work has been researched through technical reports, contemporary sources, and through the personal recollections of retired employees and others. David's objective was simply to record what he believed to have been an important era in history, as it related to his home town, in a dispassionate and objective manner.

On reading the manuscript, we in the Trust felt that this was an important piece of work deserving of a wider audience. Despite the fact that the book is not specifically about Rolls-Royce, it records the foundations on which the Company was later to build its reputation at Barnoldswick, as well as paying due homage to all the companies involved.

We are grateful to David Brooks for allowing us to publish this book in the Historical Series.

Richard Haigh
Chief Executive, Rolls-Royce Heritage Trust

PREFACE

During the early part of the Second World War, important and highly secret development work on the Whittle gas turbine aero-engine was transferred to the small town of Clitheroe, in the North West of England, in order to secure a safer relocation for the work, away from the major industrial centres in the Midlands which had become prime targets for enemy bombing.

The most important period of activity at the requisitioned Waterloo Mill in the town, lasted for a little under two years between 1941 and 1943. During this relatively short period of time, the factory was host to one of the half-dozen or so teams of development engineers then working on the gas turbine aero-engine in this country. This account traces the events leading up to the move to Lancashire, the progress made in the development work and some of the problems which had to be overcome.

Reference is also made to some of the leading personalities involved and to the events which resulted in significant changes taking place in 1943. Related aspects of the subsequent history of the gas turbine aero-engine development programme and of other activities on the Waterloo Mill site are also briefly outlined. The personal difficulties which arose between the leading figures at Power Jets and Rover, and also between different factions within the Air Ministry, led to a polarisation of views by many of the senior personnel directly involved with the work. The depth and intensity of feeling which built up at that time can still be sensed in a number of the written accounts which relate to the period, and lead to inevitable difficulties when attempting to present a fair and balanced narrative.

Some of the contemporary records, which were consulted during the research for this work, provided information which revealed some important factual inaccuracies and misleading statements in a number of the previously-published accounts of the Rover Company's involvement with the Whittle engine. It is hoped therefore that, with the inclusion of the new material, this account might contribute towards a wider appreciation and more comprehensive understanding of this period of gas turbine development, as well as fulfilling its primary aim of recording local history.

The author would be pleased to receive any further information or comments relating to the events covered in this account.

David S Brooks
Clitheroe
December 1996

VIKINGS AT WATERLOO

CHAPTER 1

THE BACKGROUND

In the field of engineering, as elsewhere, the development of innovative ideas and schemes into reliable and economically viable systems seldom takes place smoothly or within the time frame which might ideally be hoped for. Practical difficulties, which might or might not have been foreseen, can impose limitations or delays, or even result in a particular line of development coming to a premature halt. Such difficulties arose when proposals were first considered to utilise the principle of the gas turbine as a radically new power source for aircraft in the 1920s.

The first successful powered-and-piloted flights made by the Wright brothers in 1903 had employed the petrol-fuelled internal combustion engine – a relatively reliable power source which was already being successfully used in the infant automobile industry. Over the next two decades progress in airframe and engine design had been rapid, with the First World War acting as the catalyst for much of this development. Alternative means of propulsion, which would enable greater forward speeds for aircraft, were being studied. One possible solution which was being considered by a number of engineers at that time was the gas turbine.

The three principles behind the basic concept – jet reaction, jet propulsion and the turbine, had individually been thought through and demonstrated over a long period of time. Indeed, the turbine itself had already been very successfully utilised in a number of industrial applications.

Much of the thought during this period was orientated towards the turbine as a device which might drive a propeller (an arrangement widely used many years later and subsequently known as the 'turboprop'). The idea of having a turbine which would drive a compressor linked to a combustion chamber to produce a jet of air was not generally recognised.

The established aero-engine manufacturers in this country rejected the gas turbine as a new power source for aircraft however. The great majority of engineers and scientists who had studied the problem concluded that the idea was impracticable on two main counts – non-availability of suitable materials and a general belief that the necessary aerodynamic efficiences were unattainable.

The earliest proposal to use the gas turbine as a propulsive system in its own right was made in this country in a report written in 1926 by Dr A A Griffith of the Royal Aircraft Establishment.

At roughly the same time, a young Royal Air Force flight cadet, by the name of Frank Whittle, (later to become Air Commodore Sir Frank Whittle), started to consider the possibilities of jet flight whilst completing a course at the RAF College, Cranwell, in 1928. From then on he began to develop his ideas of utilising the gas turbine for aircraft propulsion. Almost alone at that time, he appreciated that the gas turbine could be used to provide a jet of air which would propel an aircraft but he experienced great difficulty in convincing others of the soundness of his proposals. Nevertheless, by 1936 his work had progressed to the stage where, with the assistance of two fellow ex-RAF officers, he had formed the company of Power Jets in order to develop these ideas further and to produce a practical engine.

Power Jets did not have the facilities to produce the components for the new engine design and so contracts were placed with other companies. One of the firms which had been approached, because of their experience in steam turbine design and manufacture, was the British Thomson-Houston Company (BTH) of Rugby. These early contacts led to permission being given by BTH for Power Jets to use a section of the BTH premises where the first of a series of experimental jet engines could be tested. Much assistance was given to Power Jets by the BTH company in those early days but,

The Whittle Experimental Engine after its second reconstruction – circa 1938.
The car engine mounted on the test trolley, to the left of the photograph, was used for starting the gas turbine at that time.

nevertheless, the fledgling company led by Frank Whittle was frequently working under considerable financial difficulties and with minimal assembly and testing facilities.

This first design for the 'Whittle Experimental Engine' consisted of a single combustion chamber and was referred to as the WU engine – an abbreviation for 'Whittle Unit'. It had its first test run on 12 April 1937.

At about this time, the chief engineer of BTH agreed to allow Power Jets to rent alternative premises on a part of the disused BTH foundry, known as the Ladywood Works. This was situated at Lutterworth – some seven miles north-east of Rugby and became the new site for the engine testing and development work of Frank Whittle's team. Following various delays, it was almost a year after the first test run of the WU engine before testing resumed with a reconstructed engine. This only lasted for a short time because, on 6 May 1938, when running at some 13000 rpm, there was a disastrous failure of the turbine which wrecked the engine.

After a second major reconstruction of the WU engine, which included a modification to incorporate ten small combustion chambers in place of the previous arrangement, testing was resumed at the end of October 1938. As a result of these tests the Air Ministry awarded a contract to Power Jets for a flight engine, known as the W1, and also for a new and more powerful engine which was designated the W2.

By early 1940 work on the W1 engine was well advanced. The task of constructing the engine had been subcontracted to the BTH company by Power Jets, who would carry out the actual testing themselves once the engine had been completed. Meanwhile the design of the new W2 engine was progressing favourably.

The relationship between Whittle and the BTH company became less cordial at about this time, and Whittle decided that he wanted to find other firms to use as subcontractors for the manufacture of components for his W2 engine. The wife of J C B Tinling, one of Whittle's associates at Power Jets, was a close friend of the wife of Maurice Wilks, chief engineer of the Rover Motor Company. This link led to a meeting between Whittle and Wilks in January 1940 at which Whittle suggested that Power Jets might place contracts with the Rover Company. Accordingly Maurice Wilks promised to discuss the suggestion with his brother Spencer Wilks who was Managing Director of Rover.

The Wilks brothers met Whittle and three of his associates at the Rover works shortly afterwards. During the course of the meeting the team from Power Jets offered a substantial financial stake in their company and Spencer Wilks, at Whittle's suggestion, approached officials at the Air Ministry to discuss the proposition. This contact produced immediate repercussions and before a definite decision had been reached a letter was received at Rover from the Air Ministry stating that firms who already had an interest in Power Jets should have no difficulty in providing further finance.

A meeting was called by the Air Ministry in late March 1940 to which Frank Whittle and the Wilks brothers were invited to attend. Ministry officials pointed out that, as Frank Whittle was a serving RAF officer, the Crown had free use of Power Jets' patents and that Power Jets therefore had nothing to offer in return for finance.

Negotiations for a financial link between the two companies finally collapsed at a later meeting between Whittle and S B Wilks at the home of the latter on 31 March. This inauspicious attempt to link the Rover Company financially to the pioneering work of Power Jets presaged the much greater difficulties which were later to arise between the two companies. For the moment however, the failure was deeply disappointing to Whittle and his associates at Power Jets.

Whittle had informed the Air Ministry of his earlier meeting with the Wilks brothers and his proposal to use the Rover Company as subcontractors. He was completely taken aback however when he was informed that the Air Ministry had themselves decided to invite the Rover Company to participate in the development programme by giving them direct contracts for the construction of development engines of his design.

At a later meeting, in April 1940, he was further informed by the Air Ministry that Rover, together with the BTH company, would also be given direct contracts for production engines. The Air Ministry had decided that Power Jets should continue with its work under Whittle, but only as a research and development organisation, whilst other firms, who they considered to be in a better position and more able to carry out the work, would be given the task of engine production.

Air Commodore Frank Whittle

Whittle and his fellow directors felt much aggrieved by these Ministry decisions believing that Power Jets should have been awarded the contracts for development and production engines. They reasoned that this was the logical way forward as the company was the only one with the necessary expertise, and, additionally, that they had conducted all the early experimental and development work so far carried out in this country. From that time, the relationship between Whittle and the Rover Company was soured, but deteriorated much further as subsequent policy decisions were made by the Ministry and later events unfolded.

Following representations from Power Jets the Ministry decided that the Whittle design should be adhered to and that the Rover company should only make minor modifications which would ease production of the engine.

At about this time, Whittle realised that he had made errors in the design calculations for the W2 engine then being constructed and that it would require redesign. Although construction continued on the W2 units, work was put in hand on the modified design which subsequently carried the designation W2B, the 'B' signifying a major revision of the W2 design.

Whilst the Rover Company had considerable engineering expertise with motor cars, they fully appreciated that there were aspects of the new work in which they had no experience on which to draw to overcome the problems posed by the development of the Whittle gas turbine. Much of the technology required had, in fact, to be specially developed as the combustion requirements of the engine, and the materials used in the manufacture of certain components, were beyond the limits of technological knowledge and understanding at that time.

The Whittle gas turbine, or 'jet engine' as it became more familiarly known, had three major aspects :-

the compressor and turbine – running on the same shaft,
the fuel control system,
the combustion and exhaust system.

Rover decided that they would manufacture the compressor/turbine assembly themselves, that they would sub-contract the fuel and combustion sections to a specialist company, and that they themselves would assemble and test the complete engine. With the Ministry's approval, Rover chose the firm of Joseph Lucas as main sub-contractor, a company with whom they had had close co-operation on many occasions in the past. They considered this choice a particularly appropriate one since C A Vandervell (CAV), a subsidiary of the Lucas Company, had considerable experience in fuel injection systems, whilst Lucas themselves had much expertise in sheet metal working.

The course of the war in France and Belgium now began to have a direct influence on the gas turbine development programmes. During May 1940, with the British Expeditionary Force about to be evacuated from Dunkirk, an urgent order was despatched from the Ministry to Rover (and the other companies involved in the project), to the effect that all priority was to be immediately removed from work on the Whittle engine. The reasoning behind this move was that a concerted effort was deemed necessary on fighter and piston engine production to counter the threatened enemy invasion of the country. The effect of the order was to practically bring to a standstill the manufacture of parts for the experimental engines, but, at Rover, a skeleton team of about six drawing office staff continued to work on the project. It was to be almost year-end before priority was once again restored to the project and normal working could resume.

At that time the main facilities of the Rover Company were being fully utilised for the more general war work which they were undertaking and 'Shadow Factories' had been developed for the production of Bristol aero-engines. Preparatory work on the development Whittle engines had already started but pressure was mounting to find other premises where the production of the gas turbine engines could take place.

A meeting of the Rover Directors was held in September 1940 at which Spencer Wilks reported that he had approached the Ministry with a suggestion that alternative accommodation should be found for the company's manufacture, in case the main works were damaged by enemy action. He went on to say that the Minister, Lord Beaverbrook, had given authority for the necessary steps to be taken to secure premises in a safer area.

Mr A Bernard Smith who was, at that time, the Buyer and Stores Controller for the Rover Shadow Factories then involved in making Bristol aero-engines, recalls that in the late summer of 1940 he received an urgent telephone call from Geoffrey Savage (later Sir Geoffrey Savage), Rover's Production Director. The instructions were for him to get out a map, draw a line from Lancaster to Grimsby, find a factory ready to occupy north of that line and not to return until he had found it!

On setting up his base at Lancaster Mr Smith worked along the industrial sites of the Lune valley. When recalling the events some fifty years later, he remembered that the heavy chemical plants which he inspected choked him to death – much to the amusement of managers who enjoyed 'dousing his ardour', and thus protecting their premises from any possible requisition.

Meeting with no success in that area he decided to advertise in the northern newspapers. One of his advertisements, which appeared in The Manchester Guardian of 12 September 1940, read :-

> MILLS, MANUFACTORIES, WORKS, &c – WANTED
> Factory Premises Wanted, ground floor about 300 000 sq ft or reasonable proportion of the area, in North Lancashire District. Information to A B Smith, c.o. County Hotel, Lancaster.

A post-war aerial view of Bankfield Shed, Barnoldswick.

The advertisements elicited a reply which led to a meeting between Mr Smith and his respondent at the Black Horse Hotel in Skipton, where he had set up a new base after moving on from Lancaster.

He had already discovered that there were a number of weaving sheds available in the area but had found them too small for the Rover Company's requirements. When his communicant revealed that he knew of a suitable weaving shed, he felt that his time was about to be wasted. However his visitor drew his attention to the Bankfield Shed at Barnoldswick which was a double unit and therefore much larger than other factories in the area. Better still, it had been bought by Messrs British Celanese Ltd, and had just been cleaned up and re-decorated for their own use. With a floor area of some 165 000 sq ft it was somewhat smaller than originally envisaged, but, in most other respects, proved to be the ideal factory – being ready for occupation and having extra room for extension. Thus it was that a requisition order, dated 25 September 1940, was formally signed for the Bankfield Shed.

Initially, the premises were said to be needed for the piston aero-engine work being carried out by the company, but this aspect of Rover's work was soon transferred to other sites and Bankfield became the centre for the proposed production of the Whittle gas turbine engines. The newly-acquired site was officially referred to as 'Number 6 Shadow Factory' in company minutes. This reflected the Ministry's preference for the work to be carried out on a 'Shadow' basis, ie with the factory being managed by Rover staff but with all expenses paid by the Ministry. Later internal documentation tends to refer to it simply as the 'No 6 Factory' but it was more commonly referred to in day-to-day correspondence etc, by simply using its name - 'Bankfield Shed', frequently shortened to just 'Bankfield'.

With the establishment of a Rover base at Barnoldswick, a check was made of other buildings in the area for use as dispersal premises for the other war work which was being undertaken by Rover. As a result, a number of additional units were set up for the company's other war contracts, which included the production and repair of Armstrong Siddeley Cheetah aero-engines and the manufacture of airframe parts for the Armstrong Whitworth Albermarle bomber.

The 'North West group of factories', as they were later referred to, included Grove Mill and Soughbridge Mill in Earby, Calf Hall Mill and Butts Mill in Barnoldswick and Carleton Mill near Skipton. Bracewell Hall, between Barnoldswick and Gisburn, was taken over to serve as the

Bracewell Hall situated between Barnoldswick and Gisburn – taken over by the Rover Company as the administrative centre for the 'North-West group of factories'.
(Barnoldswick Local History Group – via Lancashire Library).

administrative centre for the group, and Waterloo Mill, in Clitheroe, was also to become a member of this cluster.

Meanwhile, the events of the night of 14 November 1940 demonstrated the importance of Spencer Wilks' earlier moves to secure alternative factory accommodation in safer areas. On that night, the city of Coventry was the target for an eleven-hour raid by German bombers causing widespread destruction and during which the Rover factory was severely damaged. The situation was such that there was now an immediate requirement for new premises to re-locate the Rover Company's work from Helen Street. The management, administration and engineering department staffs were moved out to a pre-arranged emergency site at the Chesford Grange Hotel, a large country-house between Kenilworth and Leamington, where many of the departments were to stay for the remainder of the war. Assembly of the first Rover-built W2 engine was completed here, prior to delivery to Power Jets, but the recently requisitioned 'safer locations' in the North West were now quickly needed for the jet engineering and production teams.

CHAPTER 2

CLITHEROE ENTERS THE STORY

At the beginning of the war, a sizable number of old textile factories were lying empty in North East Lancashire and surrounding districts, following the difficult trading period of the 1930s. Whilst not always the ideal premises for the war-work which was subsequently planned, they provided a ready-built, and therefore quickly occupyable, source of accommodation for the urgently needed war production.

In the search for extra accommodation by the Rover Company, a small disused weaving mill was found in Clitheroe and considered suitable for the requirements of the Company. The mill, officially referred to as Waterloo Mill, but better known to local people as 'Th' Back Factory', offered some 24000 sq ft of floor space. The factory had been disused for some ten years following closure during the poor trading conditions of the 1930s. Before that time it had been utilised for many years by Messrs Duckworth and Eddlestone as a weaving shed although, when opened in the mid-nineteenth century, it had been built as a spinning-mill.

Shortly before being requisitioned the building had been acquired by the Lancaster Hosiery Company, a subsidiary of the Middlebrook Manufacturing Company of Manchester, but the needs of the war effort were paramount. It was quickly decided that Waterloo Mill would be utilised as the site where Rover would make the prototype parts for the turbine, and carry out assembly and experimental testing, whilst Lucas would manufacture prototype and production combustion systems. In this way the old textile mill on the eastern fringes of the town was taken over as one of the Rover dispersal sites, (possibly number 7), and became involved in the evolution of the jet engine at a key stage in its development.

Waterloo Mill was earmarked for the Rover Jet Engineering Team towards the end of 1940. A report presented to the Rover Board of Directors on 26 November 1940 gave the information that all of the 'Whittle Engine Development Work', temporarily housed at Chesford Grange at that particular time, was to be transferred to the Dispersal Factory of Waterloo Mill once repairs and alterations had been carried out there. It was thought that the work would take approximately two months to complete but this estimate proved to be too optimistic.

Steps were taken in the first weeks of 1941 to secure accommodation for the workers who would transfer from Coventry and elsewhere. At this time, some two years into the war, there were already considerable numbers of additional military personnel stationed in the town on war duties, particularly those connected with the training establishment of the Royal Engineers at the

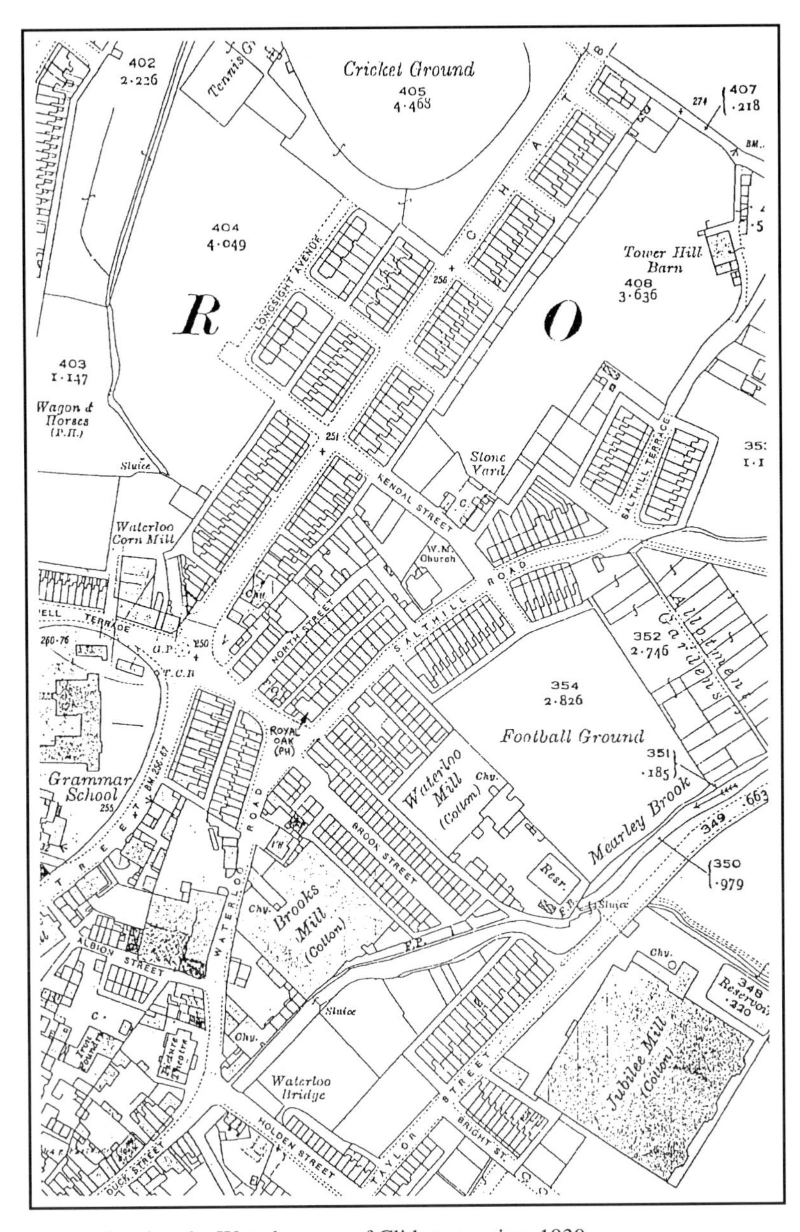

A map showing the Waterloo area of Clitheroe – circa 1930

Low Moor Mill. There was also a sizable number of evacuated families.

In a conversation which took place on 3 January between a Rover welfare officer and the Clitheroe town clerk, it was pointed out that, in addition to the Rover personnel who would be transferring from Coventry, other workers would shortly be arriving for the ICI and Bristol works which were being established in the town. The municipal officer was therefore informed that some 1000 workers were expected to be moving into the area with immediate accommodation being required for some 400 workers.

The local newspaper carried a report of the subsequent town council meeting at which the request for accommodation for the 400 workers was made by the chairman of the borough's Finance and General Purposes Committee. He added the warning that compulsory powers would have to be sought if sufficient accommodation was not forthcoming voluntarily.

Shortly afterwards, a letter was received by the town clerk in which a very embarrassed Rover official admitted that the wrong information had been supplied and that, in fact, only 28 workers were expected initially! The press report of the following council meeting carried the comments of the same worthy gentleman who had spoken on the matter at the earlier meeting – but no mention of the revised information. The councillor said that he was pleased to report that his recent appeal for accommodation had met with success, quite as much as he had hoped for. He went on to say that since his appeal, a number of people had been to the Borough Treasurer's office and offered accommodation and that, up to that time, they had been able to find accommodation for all the workpeople who required it! The council chamber was reported to have resounded to calls of 'Hear, hear,' from fellow councillors!

As the workforce built up over the coming months however, accommodation did in reality become quite a serious problem and the surrounding towns and villages were scoured for suitable billeting. There was a continuous struggle to find sufficient accommodation for the workforce, and lodgings and requisitioned housing were eventually found in locations stretching from Blackburn in the south, to Rimington, Twiston and Sawley in the north.

The building firm of Higgs and Hill was awarded the contract to prepare the factory for its new use and work progressed rapidly over the early months of 1941. By Easter much of the preparatory work was well on the way towards completion and the premises could already accommodate the earliest arrivals. Workers began to be drafted in from the Clitheroe area and further afield to supplement the core of skilled personnel transferred from the Rover parent company in Coventry and from Joseph Lucas in Birmingham.

In February 1941 the Ministry of Aircraft Production, (MAP), who from May 1940 had taken over the technical departments of the Air Ministry, decided that the Rover Company should proceed to provide capacity for the production of twenty W2B engines per week. This decision by the Ministry, to plan production contracts for the new engine which, whilst promising much, was still some considerable time away from its first test run and at a very early stage of development, was ultimately to lead to substantial difficulties when early expectations regarding production schedules were not met.

Meanwhile, in great secrecy, preparations were being made for an important first flight of the research aircraft which would be powered by one of the earlier Whittle W1 engines.

CHAPTER 3

AN HISTORIC FIRST FLIGHT

In early 1941 the W1 engine was under construction by BTH and nearing completion. Meanwhile, a similar engine was being assembled by BTH using a spare rotor from the earlier experimental engine and other W1 components. This latter engine, known as the W1X, was intended to test engine installation and enable ground handling tests to be carried out prior to the availability of the W1 flight engine. During the early months of 1941 it was installed in the experimental aeroplane which had been specially designed by the Gloster Aircraft Company to test the new jet engines then being constructed. This important historic aircraft, which is now preserved in the Science Museum in London, was designated the Gloster-Whittle E28/39. It had the W1X engine installed and began taxying trials in the weeks prior to its first flight with the W1 engine installed.

The historic flight, the first by a jet-powered aircraft in Britain, took place at the Royal Air Force airfield of Cranwell on 15 May 1941. By coincidence, the flight occurred at virtually the same time as the Rover and Lucas companies were first taking up their occupation of the Waterloo Mill site in Clitheroe.

The first Gloster-Whittle E28/39 research aircraft.

Meanwhile, the improved and more powerful W2 engine was being built by the Rover Company. Another version of this engine was also being built by BTH but this had been modified to the W2B standard and was designated W2 Mk IV. The testing of this latter engine began in July 1941 but ended abruptly following an explosion caused by an impeller failure in October of the same year.

The first of the two W2 engines built by Rover was required to be sent to Power Jets for testing and this was despatched in April/May 1941 from Chesford Grange where the work had been carried out. Some time later it was returned to Rover and they continued to work on it for a short time.

The successful first flight of the E28/39 provided a spur to other manufacturers who were party to the secret developments being undertaken by Power Jets and who had been invited to participate in various aspects of the gas turbine programme by the Air Ministry. At the invitation of the Royal Aircraft Establishment (RAE) the firm of Metropolitan-Vickers Ltd had been assisting in the construction of the RAE's own design of gas turbine engine since 1939, and in January 1941 the firm of de Havilland was invited to design a jet fighter together with an engine to power it. Each of these projects followed quite independent lines but drew on the experience of Power Jets.

At that time Rolls-Royce was very heavily committed with the development and production of the Merlin piston engine and was not amongst the companies invited to participate in the new work. They had however taken Dr A A Griffith on to their technical staff in 1939 and he was working on a much more complex axial-flow design of engine which was seen as a long-term project. As mentioned previously, Dr Griffith was one of the leading authorities on gas turbines at that time having been head of the Engine Department at the RAE.

As with other leading British aero-engine manufacturers, it had been arranged that some of the senior Rolls-Royce engineers should visit Power Jets at Lutterworth to see the WU engine under test. From these visits a liaison was established with Frank Whittle which served a useful mutual purpose. On the one hand it kept the Rolls-Royce management informed on the progress with the Whittle engine, whilst on the other the experimental shop at Rolls-Royce's Derby works was able to give help with the production of certain engine components for Power Jets. In addition, a test rig was also constructed at Derby where the compressor of the Whittle engine could be tested. Up to then no rigs of sufficient power had existed in this country.

The general feeling of the senior Rolls-Royce management at this time was that the development of gas turbines was a long term project and that it was unlikely that the work would seriously affect the outcome of the war. However, a somewhat closer involvement in gas turbine work was secured when Rolls-Royce subsequently arranged to design their own version of the

Whittle engine, subsequently known as the WR1, based on Frank Whittle's W2B design.

These various excursions into gas turbine design and development by Rolls-Royce were to provide an important factor in the company's subsequent involvement in the wider jet engine programme some two years later.

CHAPTER 4

WORK BEGINS AT WATERLOO MILL – FIRST ARRIVALS

The history of the Lucas Company records that the Waterloo Mill premises were ready for occupation in May 1941. However, the first workers had started to arrive in late March and early April whilst building alterations were still being made. Even earlier, a small number of men and women from the Rover and Lucas Companies had been actively engaged in the town from January 1941. They had been given the task of making the necessary preparations for the new venture prior to the arrival of the main body of workers.

Of the personnel who would staff the offices and workshops at Waterloo, the initial Lucas group of shop-floor workers were the first to arrive at the factory as it was in the final stages of preparation. They proceeded to set up occupation in what was thought to be the more attractive section of the works, much to the annoyance of the Rover personnel who arrived shortly afterwards, and who were, of course, the 'senior' partners. A little tactful re-location was quickly made and harmony restored.

Back Brook Street – the main approach to Waterloo Mill. *(Author).*

Early alterations to the old textile mill included the conversion of the warehouse and first-floor area above the boiler room into office accommodation, the division of the weaving shed into two separate units (one for each of the Rover and Lucas teams), the construction of a two storey office/workshop extension close to the old factory engine room, and an engine test-house in the mill yard nearby. Despite the additional buildings however, space was at a premium and office accommodation was even provided in part of the old water tower at a later period.

In this initial stage of occupation at Waterloo Mill, the plan was for the Lucas Company to use the premises as an experimental sheet-metal section for the manufacture of the combustion system. Experience quickly showed that much more space would be required for this work and led to the transfer of this section away from the mill at the end of 1941. The company still retained a presence on parts of the site however as will be recounted later. In the eight months during which the sheet-metal section was based at Waterloo Mill, work was undertaken for the parent Birmingham factory and for the Rover Company, as well as a small amount for Power Jets and BTH.

The Lucas team which transferred to Clitheroe from the Company's works in Birmingham comprised about twenty men led by S A (Sammy) Mason. He had previously worked on the development of the combustion system for the early jet engine work at the Great King Street factory in Birmingham.

One of the senior members of the Lucas workforce accompanying Sammy Mason from Birmingham was Frank Coxson. He acted as works superintendent for Lucas at Waterloo Mill, and had general responsibility for its day-to-day running. Another engineer who transferred from combustion development at Shaftmoor Lane Birmingham, was J J (Joe) Righton. His role at Clitheroe was as development engineer with responsibility for liaison on combustion work with the Rover team. He was later to be promoted to senior management in the Lucas company when he became General Manager at Burnley in the post-war period and, later still, Group Technical Director.

The entrance gate leading to the mill yard. *(Author).*

Other early arrivals with the Lucas team included Alf Huyton as chief draughtsman who transferred from the drawing office at Great King Street Birmingham together with one of his draughtsmen, Harold Simpson. Tommy Kirk came in charge of administration, and Dennis Jones, an experienced sheet-metal worker who had been seconded from the firm of Fisher and Ludlow, was put in charge of the sheet-metal section.

Extra workers were soon drafted in from neighbouring areas. One was Jack Gregory who had trained at the wartime Training Centre at Chester as a welder and sheet-metal worker. His association with the Clitheroe site was to last much longer than most of his contemporaries when, in post-war days, he returned from the Lucas works in Burnley to become works superintendent of the Clitheroe factory until his retirement in 1977, which coincided with the time when the company finally moved out of the town. As the work progressed other skilled and semi-skilled workers were drawn from the surrounding areas with men coming from Accrington, Burnley, Preston and other neighbouring towns, as well as from much further afield.

The sections eventually set up within the Lucas part of the factory included – a small press shop, a welding section and a machine shop, although by far the greatest area was laid out for the sheet-metal workers. On their arrival at Waterloo Mill however, the first group of men found the workspace to be completely empty and lacking the benches, tools and materials which they had expected would be awaiting them.

One of the first tasks was the aquisition of work benches. These were ordered from and supplied by a local timber merchant, Luke Smalley of Chatburn. Another local supplier who was called upon to provide some of the small hand-tools which would be required was the Clitheroe ironmonger, Theo Wilson. Subsequent experience showed that some of these early purchases from Theo's were quite unsuitable for working on the stainless steel sheet-metal which arrived shortly afterwards. It is said that the one good pair of snips which had been brought by Dennis Jones were very much in demand in those early days!

The need for more sheet-metal workers was such that five local men who had earlier worked as tin-smiths for Theo Wilson were commandeered. Their skills, which had been utilised in the repair of milk kits for the local farmers, were quickly adapted to the new task in hand.

Eventually equipment and drawings arrived, as did the heavy tools for the machine shop. The main task of the sheet-metal team was the construction of the combustion chambers, or 'cans' as they became more familiarly known, for the W2B engine. The work involved some difficult and complicated shaping of the stainless steel, and, since very few of the men had previous experience of working with this material, the men acquired the necessary skills as the work proceeded.

The first impression of tool maker Arthur Neal, who joined the team at that time, was of the deafening noise resulting from the beating of the sheet-metal and of a 'Heath Robinson' set-up with men in bib-and-braces overalls, as opposed to the white coats he was accustomed to in the tool-room. It amazed him to find the sheet-metal workers fashioning the components using moulds made from tree trunks. Harry Tegerdine, another early recruit in the welding and sheet-metal team, recalled that this latter technique was used when trying to shape some of the more difficult curves in the stainless steel. A section of a tree trunk would be prepared by having a suitable hollow hammered into it with a heavy hammer and this was then used to shape the intricate bend by beating the sheet-metal into the hollow. This technique was later superseded by the use of sand bags.

The Lucas team of workers remained completely separate and independent from the Rover personnel in their own half of the old weaving shed and it is recalled that, in the early stages, they were not even aware that they were involved in the same work as their neighbours in the Rover team.

In assembling the ten combustion chambers into the annular arrangement for the engine, they were first made as a set of ten separate cans before being joined into pairs by welding. The pairs of cans were then formed into a four and into a six before finally being brought together on a special jig to make up the full arrangement of ten cans. On one occasion, remembered by Harry Tegerdine, Sammy Mason walked down the shop just as two workmen were using a heavy hand to force the two sets of cans into the correct position for welding. His comments, made in forceful terms to the workmen concerned, suggested that their skills were more appropriate to a blacksmith's forge than a precision engineering shop!

Many problems were experienced in the manufacture and assembly of these sets of cans and are indicative of some of the early setbacks faced in the manufacturing aspects of the work. An account of some of the difficulties being experienced with these components was recalled by Frank Whittle himself in his autobiography written in 1953. He stated that, when the first Rover-built W2B engine was handed over to Power Jets as a kit of parts for assembly and testing in October 1941, many failures of the sheet-metal components hampered progress. He commented that Messrs Joseph Lucas had been given the task of producing the sheet-metal components for Rover but had not, at that time, got into their stride. He went on to say that he attributed these particular failures to manufacture rather than design.

Dr E A Watson. *(Lucas Heritage Trust).*

At that time, some of the inspection and testing techniques were quite rudimentary. One member of the early workforce remembers that, on completion of the welding, and following a visual check, the only test given to each can was a quick test which consisted of blanking off all of the holes and attaching an air-line to provide a compressed air supply. The can was then dipped into a sink full of water at the side of the shop to check whether any air bubbles could be seen.

As indicated previously, the Lucas Company had been sub-contracted to carry out two vital parts of the work – the manufacture of a combustion system together with the associated research and development, and the manufacture and development of the fuel-control system.

Dr J S Clarke. *(Lucas Heritage Trust).*

This work, particularly that aspect connected with the combustion system, was an area in which Frank Whittle himself had little experience and where he felt much less sure of his ground. The research and development work carried out at Lucas under Dr E A Watson – the Lucas Group Chief Engineer, together with Dr J S Clarke who he appointed to take charge of combustion research, provided essential knowledge and understanding of the combustion process which became a key factor contributing to the ultimate success of the venture. The research and development work carried out by the Lucas Company played a vital role in this and later projects. In their role as a major sub-contractor however, their work is often overlooked and insufficient credit given.

It had quickly been realised by the Lucas management, and by the Ministry, that Waterloo Mill was not suitable for the provision of the great amount of sheet-metal items which would be required for the rapidly expanding jet engine programme, and that new premises would be required. In June 1941 therefore, another disused textile mill was requisitioned. This time it was the Wood Top Mill in Burnley which was taken over for the exclusive use of the Lucas Company. As it had been previously damaged by fire, much reconstruction was necessary and it was not until the end of 1941 that the building was ready for occupation.

Whilst the Lucas fuel system research and development work remained with CAV at Acton in West London, and work on the burners and combustion research continued to be carried out at the Shaftmoor Lane site in Birmingham, a new combustion research laboratory was established at Wood Top, and it was to there that the experimental sheet-metal section from Waterloo Mill transferred in late December 1941. After only eight months at

Waterloo Mill, the Lucas team left to occupy their new premises over the Christmas/New Year period, with the equipment being transported over the relatively short distance by the wagons of Chris Miller of Preston. The new section thus established in Burnley remained under the general managership of Sammy Mason. Whilst the majority of the Lucas team left Clitheroe for Burnley, Joe Righton remained and played a key role as liaison engineer between Lucas and Rover.

Within a short time another group of Lucas workers arrived and took up residence at Waterloo Mill working on fuel systems. The work of this team will be considered later but, for the moment, it is necessary to return to the initial establishment of the Rover team at Waterloo.

CHAPTER 5

THE ROVER JET ENGINEERING TEAM

As already noted, the Rover workers who were relocated from Coventry arrived in Clitheroe shortly after the Lucas personnel and proceeded to set up various departments at the Waterloo Mill under the managership of the Company's chief engineer Maurice C Wilks. The task given to the Rover team was to prepare the engine for quantity production, making any changes to the design which would facilitate the manufacturing process. This remit was to subsequently bring them into conflict with Frank Whittle.

Bankfield Shed, in Barnoldswick, was ready for occupation in June 1941 by the engine production team, under the Rover Company's production engineer Olaf Poppe. The Barnoldswick unit had the responsibility for setting up production lines for the W2B engines. The plan for engine production, which, as previously noted, had been outlined in February 1941 when the W2B was still only at the design stage, was for twenty engines per week, with the intention of increasing this output to fifty engines per week. Difficulties with the engine development programme were on the horizon however, and experience was to show that this intended programme was grossly over-optimistic and would need complete reassessment as the months went by.

At Waterloo Mill, the Rover team set up a number of sections to cover the work which they planned to carry out themselves. The main sections included:-

- a combined design and detail drawing office, together with its associated print room,
- the engine test department,
- associated technical and administrative offices,
- a small machine shop,
- a small fitting shop,
- an engine-build (assembly) section,
- a number of other small sections including a photographic unit and an experimental laboratory.

Senior personnel who were involved in the jet-engine work under Maurice Wilks at Waterloo Mill, most of whom had worked for the Rover Company in Coventry, included :-

W Robert Boyle – assistant chief engineer,
Roland Seale – chief designer/draughtsman,

Maurice Wilks (left) and Robert Boyle. *(via Graham Robson).*

Lester A Smith	– works manager,
John Swaine	– chief test engineer,
W F Scott	– in charge of testbeds,
Albert Harris	– in charge of the workshop,
Charles Hudson	– in charge of test engine fitters,
Walter Bowron	– in charge of inspection.

Section leaders from the Coventry design office who were later to return with the Company to become leading figures in the post-war automotive design and development staff, included Joe Drinkwater, Tom Barton and Gordon Bashford.

One of the junior section leaders in the design office who transferred from Coventry and was destined to become one of the leading figures in the Rover (and later Rolls-Royce) jet-engine development programme was Adrian Lombard. Following his eventual transfer to Rolls-Royce, as will be recounted later, he ultimately rose to be Chief Engineer of the whole of Rolls-Royce and Director of Engineering (Aero Engine Division) before his early death in July 1967 at the age of 52.

Another ex-Coventry section leader on the design staff under Roland Seale was Joe Bamford. When reminiscing about these early days he recalled that he had previously worked as a design draughtsman in the body office at Rover. Like the majority of the Rover personnel, he had been transferred to Chesford Grange following the bombing of the Coventry works before moving on to Clitheroe. In his spare time he enjoyed making pen sketches of a wide range of subjects and many years later, in retirement, he published a booklet which included over a hundred examples of his early works. One of these, a view of Waterloo Mill from Upbrooks drawn in 1943, has been reproduced as the frontispiece to this work.

A senior member of staff who had previously joined Rover on secondment from the Aeronautical Inspection Directorate of the Air Ministry was John Herriot. He was later to be appointed as Development Engineer for Rover, and subsequently transferred to Rolls-Royce where he played an important role in the gas turbine development programme with that company.

As the team became established, additional specialist personnel were drawn in from other sections of the engineering industry. Three engineers were brought in from the Carrier Engineering Company. The senior member of the trio was J Sharpley Jones who, as a senior wrangler, applied his mathematical expertise to the performance aspects of design and development, and was later to have charge of the Clitheroe facility when working for Rolls-Royce. A second Carrier engineer was Clifford Seel who had extensive experience as a production engineer, specializing in high pressure systems for industrial processes.

Another experienced engineer who later joined the team was David Ballantyne. He had worked for the aero-engine firm of Armstrong Siddeley before the war, specialising on carburettors, and was to take on the role of development engineer with responsibility for engine accessories at Clitheroe.

The evacuee spirit, following two major relocations of work place by many of the core personnel within a relatively short period of time, may well have contributed to the feeling of camaraderie – 'a family atmosphere', 'a happy time', which is remembered by many of those who worked at Waterloo during this period. Similar happy memories are also shared by many of the locally-recruited workers.

Gordon Bashford who had joined Rover in the early 1930s, recalled, many years later, that in 1935, when he moved into the design department at Helen Street in Coventry, it was – 'a sort of leaky shed-type building [housing] the total drawing office staff, which included all body and chassis people, and probably amounted to no more than fifteen people.' The newly fitted-out design office at Waterloo Mill might well have seemed almost palatial by comparison.

Initially, the drawing office and print room were sited on the upper floor of the old warehouse building, but, as more draughtsmen and tracers were taken on, the department moved into the old weaving shed next to the fitting and machine shop. This move appears to have coincided with the departure of the Lucas experimental sheet-metal section to Wood Top. The relocation of the drawing office into the old weaving shed, with its traditional northern-light windows being blacked-out as an air-raid precaution, meant that work in the department had to be carried out under artificial light at all times.

Whilst design work was carried out at Waterloo Mill no major manufacturing was undertaken on site. Components which required to be cast or forged were supplied by sub-contractors, whilst forming and machining processes were carried out at Bankfield, although some of this work was also carried out at Rover's component factory at Tyseley.

The engine development work, which was the primary function of the team at Waterloo Mill, meant, of course, that the provision of an engine test-house was an early priority. The MAP had sanctioned the building of such test facilities at a much earlier stage in the project and a test-house had been constructed at the Helen Street works. This was nearing completion when it had to be abandoned following the November bombing of the city of Coventry. With the move of the engineering staff to Chesford Grange a temporary test-house was built for the Whittle W2 engine being constructed

The Type I test house at Waterloo Mill – circa 1942. Entrance and air intake towers.

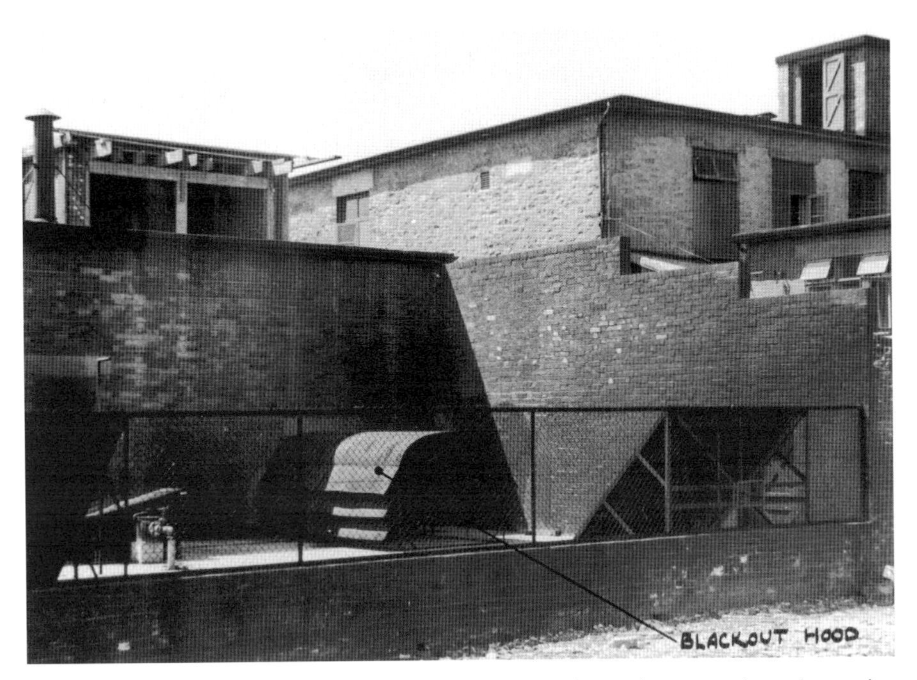

A rear view of the test house – showing the blackout hood over the test engine exhaust pipe outlet.

there by the Rover team. However, following a Ministry decision that the W2 unit should be sent to Power Jets at Lutterworth for testing, this test-house was never put to use.

Once alteration work to prepare Waterloo Mill for the Jet Engineering team had begun, a new engine test-house was constructed on the Mearley Brook side of the factory, close to the old boiler room. The test-house was orientated so that the jet exhausts pointed away from the town, towards the Upbrooks area. Construction of the building shell had already been completed by the time the first group of workers arrived and Max Alderson, then a new young Clitheroe apprentice recruit with the Rover Company, remembers helping to install the instrument panels in the test-bed control room soon after his arrival in June 1941. Much of the test equipment used was that originally intended for the test facilities at the Helen Street and Chesford Grange sites.

The test beds where complete engines could be installed, and the test rigs which enabled various components or systems to be tested, had to be designed by the Rover engineers themselves as there was very little previous

The exhaust deflector ramp with central viewing tube for observing the turbine running conditions.

experience upon which to draw for these essential test facilities. The first test-house design at Waterloo Mill was probably unique in that the engine test stands were constructed on a raft-type structure floating in a tank of water with constraints for lateral and torsional movement. This was an early attempt to incorporate means of reducing frictional losses to a minimum during engine testing and although different arrangements were devised for the later test beds at Waterloo, and also at Barnoldswick, this first engine test house, with later modifications, was successfully used throughout the war time period and beyond.

Eventually, three types of engine test-house were built at Waterloo Mill. The Type I test-house, mentioned above, was intended for performance testing. The Type II test-house was later constructed close to the tower of the old textile mill and was completed during the second half of 1942. This facility was intended for endurance testing and was rather more simple than the Type I test-house. The Type III test-house was intended as an improved version of the first type but was not completed until after the project had passed to Rolls-Royce in 1943. Further details of the engine test houses used at Waterloo Mill are given in the appendix.

The test rigs installed at Waterloo at this time included:-

accessory drive box test rigs,
a rig for testing impellors under overspeed conditions,
rigs for testing fuel pumps and jets,
rigs for testing high speed bearings.

The engine testing was, by its very nature, an extremely noisy activity. Mrs Margaret Wigglesworth (née Cramp) vividly remembers sitting at her desk in the drawing office when testing was being carried out and listening to the rising noise as the engine speed built up. She recalled that it reached the pitch where you thought that it had got to stop or there would be an explosion, but the high-pitched noise continued and seemed to go on for ever. Mrs Wigglesworth remembered that rubber ear-plugs were issued in the department for use during engine testing, though many other ex-members of staff cannot recall being issued with even these rudimentary aids.

The nearest houses to the test cells were only some forty to fifty yards away from the jet discharges – though fortunately not in a direct line! One of the residents who lived in the neighbourhood at the time described the noise of engine testing as "Hell on Earth!" Others remembered the intense frustration at not being able to escape from the prolonged and piercing noise. Some recalled that at times it became so bad that it made people feel like physically banging their heads against the wall!

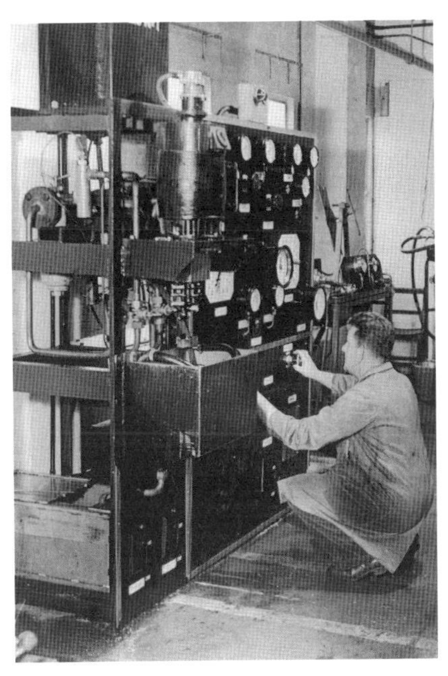

Adjustments being made to a pump test rig at Waterloo Mill.

Various attempts were made, first by Rover and later by Rolls-Royce and Lucas, to cut down the noise, but it continued to be a major problem for those living nearby. One arrangement constructed by the Rover team incorporated silencers, sometimes referred to as 'detuners', in an attempt to dissipate the noise. This detuner, which was designed and built at Waterloo Mill, was positioned where the jet pipe discharged its stream of gases into the air, and consisted of a rectangular tube with perforated lining and baffles attached to the four sides of the tube, together with a rock-wool packing. Later, other more sophisticated schemes were devised to try to overcome the noise but the problem was never totally solved.

Old Clitheronians maintain that the noise level during engine tests ensured that everyone in the town, and beyond, were fully aware of each occasion when the facility was being used. This is born out by John Swaine's recollection of a comment made by Bert Harris. He was living some ten miles out of Clitheroe at the time and stated that from his home he could clearly follow the cycles of an engine under test.

A story is still recounted about a complaint, relating to the noise of engine testing, being made in very strong terms to the management at Waterloo Mill by an influential resident of nearby Downham. Following enquiries about the precise time of the annoyance, it was ascertained that testing was only being carried out at Barnoldswick on that particular day. It is said that the conclusion that a north-easterly wind must have been blowing at the time, coupled with the knowledge that the sphere of influence of the complainant did not normally extend beyond the county boundary – as it then was, ensured that nothing further was heard of that particular incident.

At a much later date, when Rolls-Royce was in occupation at Waterloo Mill, a petition, signed by 362 residents, was sent to the Borough Council in 1944 complaining about – 'the disturbing effects of noise on the inhabitants.' The Mayor and Town Clerk interviewed representatives of the firm and efforts to minimise the noise disturbance were explained but little seems to have been done. Indeed, under the circumstances, there was probably not a great deal which could have been done considering the close proximity of factory and houses. Complaints from nearby residents were being forwarded to the council, together with periodic letters to the local press, through to the time when testing was finally ended following the removal of the Lucas fuel system team to Warwickshire in 1952.

The protestations of the neighbouring community to the noise of engine testing were not, of course, restricted to Clitheroe. The local authority in Barnoldswick received a similar string of complaints following the construction of engine test houses on the Bankfield site.

Noise was not, however, the only problem for those living nearby. Older residents remember that ornaments and framed photographs on the mantle shelves of fireplaces had to be removed during testing as the vibrations could cause them to 'dance off' and to crash to the hearth. The same vibrations also caused two of the front windows of the Co-operative Stores on Salthill Road to fall out and smash on the pavement on one occasion. Some who lived close-by also recalled that the Lancashire custom of leaving the front door 'on the latch', so that neighbours and friends could pop in, had to be abandoned as it became impossible to hear visitors when they were entering the house – whether friend or stranger. Regular visitors then had to get used to using the back doors.

Secrecy, regarding the work being carried out at the mill and of the whole project, was considered to be of the utmost importance. Information was always given on a 'need-to-know' basis and all of the ex-employees of that period who have been consulted, recalled that they never visited parts of the factory or offices with which they were not directly connected, nor indeed were they expected to do so. Workers were often unaware therefore, of the precise nature of the work being done in neighbouring departments.

The general security was such that all internal communications, as well as communications between the Ministry, Rover, Lucas and Power Jets, referred to the 'exhaust supercharger', or 'supercharger' for short, making no direct reference to the jet-engine whatsoever.

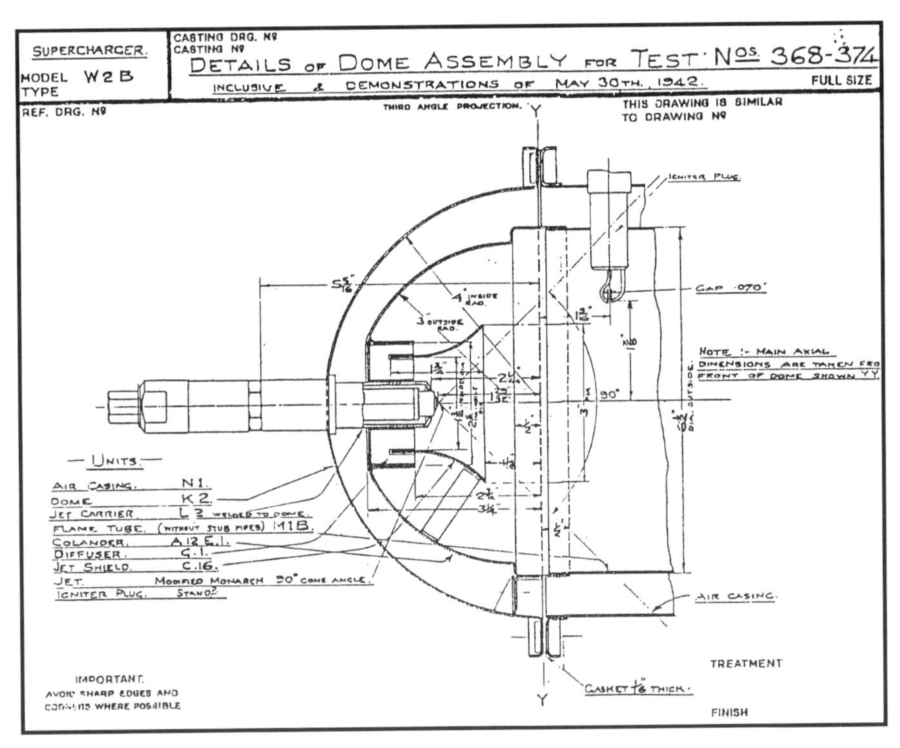

A Drawing of the combustion chamber dome assembly. Note the reference to the 'Model W2B Supercharger' (top left).

All workers had to sign a declaration of secrecy and generally lips were tightly sealed about the 'hush-hush' work being carried out at the mill. Even close members of the workers' families were not, for the most part, given details. An incident which well illustrates the general attitude towards secrecy has been recounted by Mrs Jean Shuttleworth (née Drinkwater) whose father was, as mentioned previously, a senior member of the Rover design staff. In late 1941, as a young girl in her teens, she was in the family car with her father and mother together with the chief tracer from the Rover drawing office, Miss Doris Batstone. During the course of the country run Miss Batstone mentioned something about the 'Whizzer'. Mrs Shuttleworth clearly remembers her father slamming on the brakes and turning round as white as a sheet. He proceeded to tick-off Miss Batstone severely saying she was never to say that word outside Waterloo. It meant nothing at all to Jean Drinkwater or her mother but Mr Drinkwater went on to say that if anyone was listening who might make sense of it, it could give away valuable information ... and that was just inside the family car!

The name 'Whizzer' appears to have been an early code name used within the company for the jet engine. However, a report given to the Rover Management Committee in June 1941, by its chairman Mr H Howe Graham, makes reference to the 'Wizard'. Perhaps the experiences of those employees whose work was closely connected with engine testing suggested that the former name was more appropriate, or, more probably, the code name had been mis-heard when passed on by word of mouth.

The pillbox, situated on the corner of the weaving shed roof overlooking the Back Brook Street approach to the factory. *(Author).*

The noise of testing and such clues as letter headings carrying the title – 'The Rover Company Ltd (Aero Engines)', meant that most inquisitive members of the community had a general idea of the nature of the work being carried out. Any questions which might be asked as to a more detailed explanation were likely to elicit one of the farcical explanations which were thought up from time to time to deter such questioners. One example being that they were making 'nurts for razzles', whilst another was

A view of the pillbox over the weaving shed roof. *(Author).*

that secret work was being carried out on cigarette lighters. It was recalled by one of the ex-employees many years later that, ironically, this latter explanation had more than a grain of truth in it, as cigarette lighters were one of the more popular 'foreigners' produced in the workshops at that time!

As in most large industrial plants throughout the country, a platoon of the Home Guard was formed at Waterloo Mill during 1941, with Ted Broom as the lieutenant. He was one of the workers who had been 'bombed out' in Coventry, and who subsequently worked on engine build and as storekeeper in a special compound which was constructed at the rear of the fitting and machine shop.

These part-time soldiers of the Home Guard were kept quite separate from other Home Guard units within the town, presumably because of the secret nature of the work being carried out on the premises, and the need to restrict entry to the site. Some of the guard duties of the Home Guard unit were carried out from the pillbox on the premises. This was erected on the roof of the old weaving shed on the corner nearest to the Royal Oak public house. Access to the pillbox was gained by crossing over the roof of the weaving shed, ducking under the pillbox's concrete base, which was supported above the sloping shed roof, and climbing up through an aperture into the confined space above. No other defensive structures are thought to have been erected on the site and one imagines that, in the event of an invasion, it would have been considered most unsporting of the enemy to have approached from any other direction than via the Royal Oak!

In common with all other industrial premises at that period of the war, members of the workforce were involved in 'fire-watching' duties. At one period of the war, the accommodation for these night-long activities was provided in a room at the top of the stone water tower. A bunk bed had been provided for the use of those on duty, but there was little else in material comforts. Frank Foreman, who worked as a fitter in the Experimental Laboratory and who had spent many nights on duty as one of the fire watchers, recalled that the top of the tower was the normal vantage point for viewing the night sky over Manchester, during the heavier bombing raids on that city.

Air-raid shelters were situated at various places within the site complex but, as far as can now be remembered, no emergency evacuation of the works was ever necessary due to threatened enemy air attacks. One speedy evacuation of the typing pool and drawing office did take place however, in the latter part of 1941. Wilf Bennett, who at that time worked as the 'print room boy', and whose job involved the running-off of the technical drawing 'blue prints', remembers clearly the day when he accidentally dropped a bottle of ammonia destined for the printing machine. It is said that the rapidly spreading vapours emptied that section of the building much more quickly than any warning of imminent enemy air-raid could have achieved!

Waterloo smiles – 1943 style.
(Left to right) Nellie Forrest (Secretary), Greta Sturgess (Telephonist), Florence Limbert (Telephonist), Maureen Oxburgh (Nurse in First Aid Room), Joyce Gregory (Secretary). *(via Mrs Greta Barker).*

During the period in which the Rover Company was in occupation at Waterloo Mill, an evening class was started at the Clitheroe Technical School which led to the award of the Ordinary National Certificate in Engineering. Two of the evening lecturers at the Technical School who were drawn from the Waterloo Mill staff at that time were Adrian Lombard and Joe Bamford. Whilst not restricted to the employees at Waterloo Mill, the course was mainly attended by the young men from the factory together with a few of the young women tracers. Allan Oddie, a young local lad from Waddington, started work in the Rover drawing office in April 1942. He enrolled at the 'Clitheroe Tech' for the first year of the Ordinary National Certificate course which, he recalls, necessitated attendance on three evenings each week. A year later he was transferred to Derby to take up a Rolls-Royce

Some of the productions of the Viking Players.

apprenticeship and, like a number of other young recruits of the period, was later to work on most of that company's engines from the early gas-turbines through to the RB211.

Communications were maintained between the Rover team at Waterloo, the other northern sites and Coventry, by means of two 'post cars', Rover-built of course! The regular chauffeurs were female drivers who, together with the tracers from the drawing office, a small number of secretaries, typists and telephonists, first aid staff and a handful of workers in the photographic department, goods reception, and tool-stores, made up the female personnel at the Clitheroe works. With a total workforce at Waterloo Mill rising to over 250 during the later part of the Rover Company's involvement in the project, the proportion of males to females was approximately in the ratio of five to one. This reflected the function of the Waterloo Mill operation and contrasted with the situation at Bankfield. There, a large number of young women were trained and employed as

The Rover cricket team – circa 1942 pictured in front of the Chatburn Road pavilion, Clitheroe. Back row (left to right) ? , J McCutcheon, Horace Pye, T Edwardson, Mark French, Alf Bennett, Gordon Bashford, ? . Centre row (left to right) T Cunliffe, Stan Hall, Ted Weaver (Captain), Jack Foster, Vic Greenwood. Front row (left to right) Tom Barton, Frank Bateman, Gerry Dewhurst. *(John Bennett).*

RACE FOR CLASS "B" BOATS
(12in. x 3in. x 2in. x 6in.).

GREENDALE MILL LODGE, GRINDLETON.
SUNDAY, 10th OCTOBER, 1942 - - 3-0 p.m.

SAILING RULES, &c.

(1) Buoys will be placed such that the course of race is plain reaching (i.e., sailing square with wind) if layout of pond and direction of wind allow.
(2) Each race will be sailing from between the two starting buoys to the further bank between buoys and back.
(3) Turning to be done by cane not exceeding 4ft. long (no helping hands to give the equivalent of a longer cane). Boats may be turned as soon as within reach.
(4) Boats may be lifted from water for sail adjustment, but must be returned to water at same place (i.e., skipper must not walk while holding boat).
(5) Boats may be caned along shore (to windward) to avoid incoming craft or for other purpose, but must be pushed, not pulled. While so moving a boat, cane must not touch boat forward of amidships.
(6) Boats may be turned, or withdrawn and sail adjusted, if within caning distance of pond end, or withdrawn and a new start made for that particular board (i.e., if on return trip, restart return).
(7) Boat must be of or under regulation size. (See entry form.)
(8) Racing by elimination. (Heats of 5 boats as drawn last eliminated. Heats of 4 boats—3 boats—2 boats each. The four winners of this latter sail in pairs against each other as semi-final. The final to be best of three races similar to above heats.)
(9) Starting position to be drawn for before each race.

ENTRIES.

1.—Gull ... ... J. Bamford.
2.—Imoff II. ... ... T. Barton.
3.—Sinbad ... G. Oulianoff.
5.—Mary H. II. . E. Whateley.
7.—Sapphire II. ... A. Bryan.
9.—Janis ... ... J. R. Harnott.
11.—Hawk ... ... W. Liver.
13.—Pilot II. ... G. Bashford.
14.—Wendy II. ...W. E. James.
15.—Lucille ... ... W. Willis.
16.—Stornoway ... M. Mackay.
17.—Eagle ... ... J. D. Leather.
18.—Peeping Tom . J. Standige.
19.—Noname... ...W. R. Boyle.
20.—Mercury ... ... D. Daniels.
21.—Swan ... ... L. Sharpe.
22.—Godiva ... J. Drinkwater.
23.—Cygnet ... ... W. Green.
24.—Tinker ... ... L. Calloway.
25.—Rita ... ... J. McCutcheon.

PROGRAMME
(Times Approximate).

Until 3-0 p.m. .... Trial Sailing.
3-0 p.m. .... "B" Class Race.
4-15 p.m. (approx) .... Sailing of larger unclassified boats.
4-30 p.m. .... Race for 10in. Thames barges Class "A."
Entries on the field.

ADMISSION BY PROGRAMME - - Threepence.
All proceeds to Y.M.C.A. (Grindleton Effort).

Borough Printing Co., Ltd., Clitheroe.

The Boat Race programme for October 1942. *(Allan Oddie).*

machinists, in addition to the types of occupations outlined above, and female workers therefore constituted a higher proportion of the workforce.

Although the working hours were long, various recreational facilities were arranged for those working at Waterloo. As might be expected, these tended to be taken up to a greater extent by those who had moved into the town from other areas.

A social club was provided on Back York Street, in Clitheroe, in premises which had previously been used as a warehouse for Messrs Theo Wilson & Sons Ltd. The building, for which a tenancy agreement commenced on 16 December 1941 and lasted until 31 May 1943, still stands and is now known as the Kingdom Hall. Here, table tennis and snooker facilities were provided, with teams joining in local leagues. The names used by the table tennis teams and amateur dramatic group of that period included the name 'Viking', which, it may be recalled, was a symbol much used in the Rover Company's publicity in pre-war days and is still associated with the company name through the stylized longboat badge design. The Social Club also provided the venue for the Art and Craft exhibition in March 1942 which was organised by Joe Bamford. The local newspapers carried reports noting the very high standard of pen and water colour pictures, photographs, models of ships, wood, metal, leather, knitting and needlework items.

The more physically active male members of the workforce could join in the works' football or cricket teams at the appropriate season, whilst for others the 'boat races' provided an interesting and enjoyable test of constructional ability and skill. In this latter activity specifications were drawn up and models constructed before competitions were held on local mill lodges. Two or three of these competitive events are thought to have been held before the end of the Rover involvement in 1943. An entry charge was made and small monetary prizes were awarded to the winners with all other proceeds going to local charitable efforts.

CHAPTER 6

JET ENGINE DEVELOPMENT BY THE ROVER TEAM

At the time when the Rover Jet Development team had been preparing for the move to Clitheroe in March 1941, a set of W2B engine drawings had been handed over by Power Jets. By July, the drawings had been completed by Rover. The manufacture of six development engines was then begun at Rover's Tyseley factory because, it was said, the Lancashire factories were not at that time ready to undertake the work.

Rapid progress in setting up the establishment must have been made however because, at the end of July, Dr W R Hawthorne the Head of the Combustion Test Section at Power Jets, visited Clitheroe and reported to Frank Whittle that 'the establishment seemed to be primarily devoted to development and testing, with the main engine building work being sub-contracted.' He went on to add that it appeared to him that Waterloo Mill was 'a Rover version of the Power Jets' set-up with probably more facilities for production in the offing.'

The design for the W2B engine was being progressively revised and this led to long delays in the supply of certain drawings to Rover from Power Jets, who had retained overall control of design. The original agreement had stipulated that the Whittle design of engine should be adhered to and that only minor modifications should be made by Rover which would ease production.

Frustrated by the delays, and believing also that the original Whittle W2B design could be improved, particularly in those aspects in which they had had previous extensive experience, Rover proceeded to re-design parts of the engine including – the gear box for the auxiliary drives, the bearings, the fuel system and the compressor casing. When Frank Whittle learned about these changes in June 1941, he accused Rover of going outside their original terms of reference. In their turn, the Rover Company pointed out the long delays during which they had been waiting for drawings and suggested that they were improving those aspects of the design which they felt needed modification.

Whittle complained about these breaches to the Air Ministry and matters came to a head at a MAP meeting held in December 1941 when the relative positions of Power Jets and Rover were redefined. This, in effect, removed all previous restrictions on re-design which had originally been placed on Rover. The decision was felt to be totally unfair by Whittle and the change in policy did nothing to improve the relationship between Whittle and Rover.

Shortly after the contract for the development engines had been placed, it had been specified that the first and third Rover-made W2B engines should be delivered to Power Jets for testing, the first being delivered as a set of parts for Power Jets to assemble. Accordingly, this kit of parts was delivered to Power Jets and, following assembly, testing commenced towards the end of October 1941.

A number of difficulties arose during the assembly and testing of this engine. Those relating to the failure of sheet-metal components have already been referred to, but further difficulties were experienced when two impellers supplied by Rover had to be scrapped and replaced with one produced originally for the W2 engine.

Problems which were of a far more serious nature arose during engine testing however. At only moderate speeds the compressor stalled and the engine began to 'surge'. This was a most alarming experience for the test personnel, as it was accompanied by tremendous bangs and flames coming out of the air intake as the pressure developed by the compressor was unable to match the combustion pressure, causing the airflow to pass in the reverse direction through the engine. Once the pressure was lowered, the compressor again began to function normally and the flow reversed again, until the whole process repeated itself. When this occurred the throttle had to be quickly closed to prevent the engine destroying itself.

The problem of surging was one which was to become familiar to all involved in gas turbine development. The specific point at which engine surge commenced was related to the particular characteristics of an engine design. The amount of pressure loss which occurred in the reversed-flow arrangement of the W2B design, was said to have contributed to the surging problems in the engine. As was to be expected therefore, it occurred in the tests conducted by all three of the companies then testing the Whittle engine – Power Jets, Rover and BTH. It was to be some considerable time before means were devised to prevent the onset of surge below the engine's top design speed.

The second Rover-built W2B was first run on the Waterloo Mill test bed on 27 November 1941 but, as testing and development continued on this and successive engines into 1942, Rover, Power Jets and BTH all experienced great difficulties in their attempts to reach the design performance.

The main difficulties associated with the W2B engines at this time were :-

- surging of the engines on test at speeds well below design performance,
- the cracking of sheet-metal components, later traced to rapid high pressure buffeting,
- turbine blade failure.

These were all contributory factors towards the overall problem – an inability to meet requirements of performance, reliability and durability.

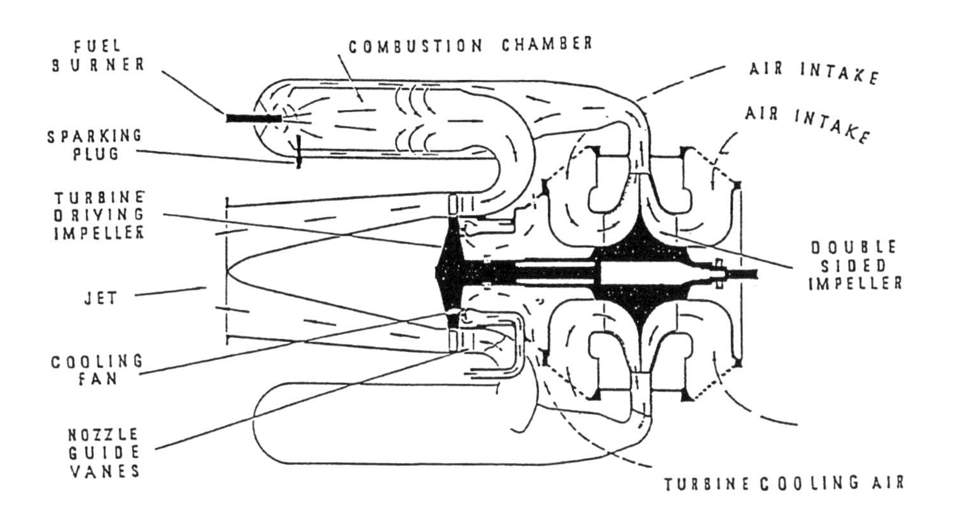

The Rover/Whittle W2B reverse-flow engine.

Although the difficulties were gradually overcome none of the work was straightforward as modifications which cured one problem often created other problems and much time had to be spent in the search for understanding and solutions.

Pressure was mounting for engines to be provided for flight trials of the prototype F9/40 aircraft built by the Gloster Aircraft Company and later to be named 'Meteor'. With performance and durability still well below that which would be required for a flight engine, a letter was despatched to Rover in mid-November 1941 from Major Bulman, Director of Engine Production at the MAP. It instructed the Rover Company to complete the first four W2B engines for flight trials at a reduced rating of not less than 1000 lb thrust and to complete the next eight engines for a thrust rating of 1200 lb.

By way of comparison, it might be noted that the power ratings of these engines were substantially greater than those obtained by the piston-engines of fighter aircraft of the day. Figures quoted by Stanley Hooker in his autobiography, refer to the Merlin engines installed in the Spitfire fighters of

A close-up view of the combustion chambers of a W2B engine showing the outer air-casing of one chamber partially cut away for instructional purposes. The Lucas 'colander' can be seen beneath the dome-end with the stub-pipes visible on the two right-hand rows of holes in the (inner) flame tube. Protruding from the end of the dome is the Lubbock burner. *(Author).*

1940/41 giving approximately 840 lb thrust.

Meanwhile, intensive investigations were being carried out by an increasing number of companies and research centres to try to solve the serious technical problems which impeded the engine's development.

Much effort was being concentrated on the combustion system at the Lucas Company in their attempt to control the burning of the fuel in the flame tubes. After a considerable amount of development, tests on the new Lucas-designed colander system of combustion chamber were completed in March 1942. The name 'colander' was adopted because of the similarity in appearance of the dome end of the flame tube to that of a domestic kitchen colander. The numerous holes in this component were the means by which the primary air supply was introduced into the flame tube. The Rover/Whittle engine equipped with this system was designated the W2B/23 – the identification which was eventually to be used for the design as taken over by the Rolls-Royce Company.

As the Rover Company was attempting to prepare engines for the projected flight trials, a great deal of difficulty was being experienced with the stub pipes through which the secondary supply of air entered the combustion chamber. The ends of these pipes were positioned in one of the hottest parts of the chamber and were unable to withstand the very high temperatures. Components were cracking or burning out during the two-hour Acceptance and half-hour Final Tests on these engines.

Attempts to pass a de-rated Acceptance Test on these engines at Waterloo Mill during the early months of 1942 had led to rejections, mainly due to low thrust and excessive jet-pipe temperatures. However, following further development work, the first of the de-rated engines passed its two-hour Acceptance Test and half-hour Final Test, and was despatched to Glosters (the manufacturer of the F9/40 aircraft) at the end of May, with a second engine following shortly afterwards.

The two engines were cleared for ground runs only, as it was doubted whether the 1000 lb thrust would provide sufficient power for safe flight. Following installation in the prototype F9/40 aircraft, the first trials were carried out on 10 July. Over the next few days the aircraft left the runway for short hops on two occasions as the pilot explored take-off performance. However, as expected, the test pilot concluded that, in the event of an engine failure on take-off, it would be impossible to climb or to maintain height. He recommended therefore that the first flight of the aircraft should be delayed until more powerful engines were made available.

Back at Waterloo Mill, and elsewhere, further work on those aspects of development which continued to impede progress towards a reliable flight engine pressed ahead. One of the major unresolved areas of difficulty lay in the production of new materials for turbine blades. Tests had shown that existing materials were unable to retain the required strength at the high temperatures reached under normal operating conditions.

A new material had been developed in the USA, under the trade name Hastelloy, and a small quantity of turbine blades manufactured in this material was delivered to Rover's Tyseley works in mid 1942. The blades were then machined, and a turbine incorporating these blades was installed in a W2B unit which was first put on test at Waterloo Mill in April/May 1942. Although the blades successfully completed some 35 hours initial running, early indications suggested that they were unlikely to stand up to long running periods in service.

Meanwhile, the MAP had turned to one of this country's leading metals companies, the Mond Nickel Company Ltd, and given them the task of solving the problem. The Mond laboratories in Birmingham went to work on developing a new alloy based on the 80% nickel-20% chromium alloy that had already been brought to the market for electrical heating elements.

The Mond laboratories were on the same site as the factory of Henry Wiggins & Company Ltd, a wholly owned subsidiary company, and they were charged with bringing the alloy from laboratory to production status. The alloy was patented and given the 'Nimonic' trade name, being known as Nimonic 80. Tests were then carried out at the National Physical Laboratory on the new Nimonic 80 alloy.

As part of the testing programme for the new alloy, the first two sets of machined turbine blades made from this material were prepared for engine testing at Waterloo Mill in July 1942. Initial results with these new blades were encouraging and promised advances over other materials tested previously. Further development work, on the new material and of the blade manufacturing process, was needed however.

It is, perhaps, worth noting here that Nimonic 80 blades were subsequently used with success by Rover, and later by Rolls-Royce, and were incorporated into post-war gas turbines made by the latter company, over a considerable number of years. These successes were still some way in the future however.

At this point, it is necessary to break off the account of the W2B development and to return to mid-1941 when other highly significant steps were being taken by the Waterloo design team.

As work on the Whittle engines progressed, it became clear to the Rover engineers that there were elements of the design which could be significantly improved, in order to facilitate production and to overcome some of the difficulties which were impeding the engine's development.

The original design evolved by Frank Whittle for the series of engines from the WU through to the W2B, had a reverse-flow arrangement whereby the air reversed direction twice after leaving the impeller before it reached

Adrian Lombard. *(via Mrs Joan Lombard).*

the turbine. This arrangement had been chosen for a number of reasons. It had originally been introduced in order to reduce the length of the shaft which connected the compressor to the turbine and so minimise the difficulties known as 'whirling', which it was known could occur with long thin shafts. Whirling in a rotating shaft can be likened to the movement of a long skipping rope when it is turned by two children standing apart from each other.

As time went on, financial limitations experienced by Power Jets, and a reluctance to alter the combustion arrangements, meant that the original design of the reversed flow remained unchanged. It was, in fact, a feature which was to be used on all of the Whittle engines which reached the production stage, including the more powerful successors of the W2B – the W2/500 and W2/700 designs.

It had been realised for some time that a more efficient arrangement would be one with a straight-through-flow system. Frank Whittle had drawn up such a design himself which he designated the W2Y. This was subsequently followed by the W3X, a later development of the modified design. However, neither of these designs progressed beyond the drawing board/mock-up stage.

At the invitation of the Air Ministry, and drawing on the earlier experience of Power Jets, Major Frank Halford at the de-Havilland Company was in the process of designing his own gas turbine with a straight-through arrangement. This was later to become the H1 engine.

Maurice Wilks was aware of some of these new straight-through flow designs and now put in hand the design of Rover's own version of this arrangement. The team responsible for the revised engine layout was led by Maurice Wilks and included his assistant Robert Boyle, together with Roland Seale and Adrian Lombard.

A new section was established at Waterloo Mill, under Adrian Lombard as project designer, with the task of preparing the detailed designs for the revised engine arrangement. The team was allocated office space above the old mill boiler-room overlooking the Type I test-house. It is recalled that this location led to considerable difficulties on the hot summer days of 1942 when staff attempted oral communication with colleagues in the office. With windows wide open to try to obtain ventilation, it became necessary, during periods of engine testing, to shout between cupped hands at a distance of two or three inches from the other person's ear in order to be heard above the noise.

There was tremendous enthusiasm amongst the Rover team for the new project, believing, as they did, that this was the eventual way forward. The team of engineers reasoned that a re-arranged flow design could simplify certain production problems and change some of the features which were felt

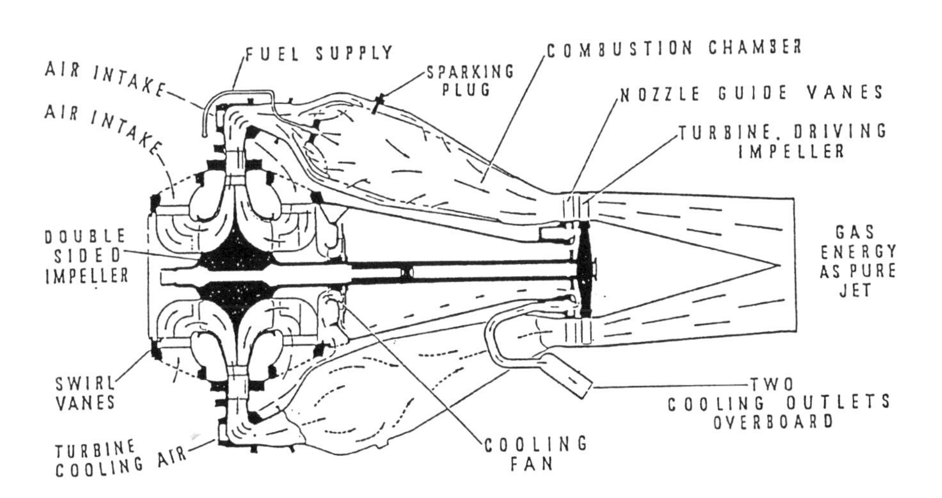

The Rover-designed W2B/26 straight-flow engine.

to be hindering the engine's development. The Rover design was known as the 'ST' (-signifying the Straight Through flow design), but was later given the official designation W2B/26, identifying it as a derivative of the original W2B design. It was, however, more often referred to within the company as the B26 or ST.

As recounted earlier, there had been a developing antagonism between Frank Whittle and the Rover management which had partially been brought about by Rover's attempts to improve aspects of the original Whittle design. There was also a reluctance to sanction major design changes in some sections of the MAP, as the Rover management had found when an earlier proposal to construct a larger engine had been turned down by the Ministry.

It was now recognised that, if the intention to design and build a straight-through variation of the Whittle engine became known to Power Jets and sections of the MAP sympathetic to them, great pressure would be brought to bear to stop such a development. Yet, as experienced engineers, the Rover design team felt certain that this should be the way forward. Accordingly the modification to the design was carried out in absolute secrecy in the Waterloo Mill design office. It has been recalled that even the Ministry's Aeronautical Inspection Directorate (AID) representative at the factory was unaware of these developments.

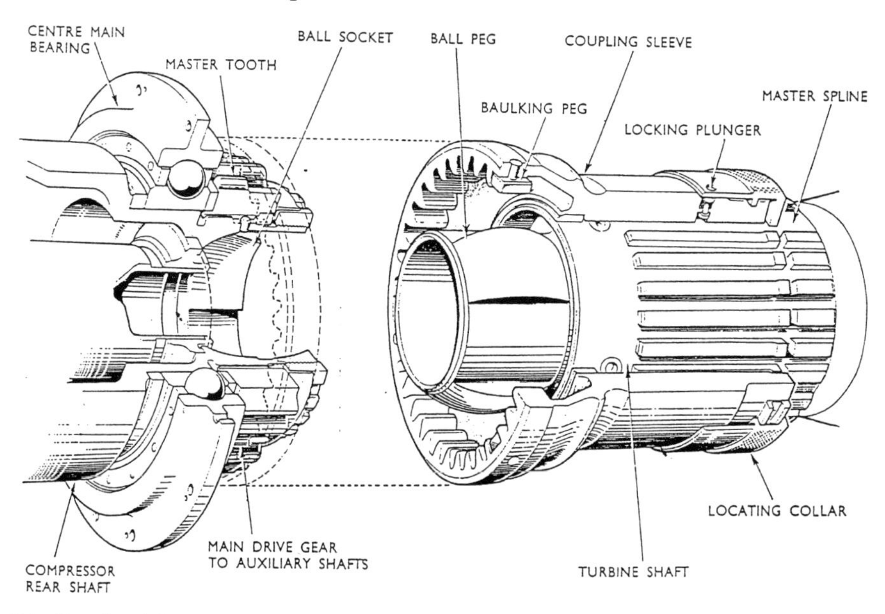

The 'Lombard Coupling' – as used on a later engine design.

The modified design was directly based on the earlier W2B and utilised major components from the earlier Whittle engine. At the front end of the engine, slight redesign was necessary on the compressor casing. This was necessary to accommodate the front-mounted burner which replaced the rear-mounted Lubbock burners on the reversed-flow arrangement, but otherwise this major component was unaltered.

The single-stage turbine and the exhaust arrangement at the rear of the engine were also retained, but the intermediate section, containing the critical combustion stage, was substantially redesigned. The Lucas Company was asked, by Rover, to produce a straight-flow combustion chamber. The opportunity was also taken to delete the stub pipes – the source of so much trouble in the W2B engine.

The problem of the long shaft was resolved by a different approach to that used by the Halford team. They had opted for a shaft of much greater diameter, thus altering the whirling characteristics to overcome potential difficulties. The Rover team produced a quite different solution to the problem. They incorporated a two-part shaft into the design between the compressor and turbine, together with a central coupling and additional bearing. The coupling, a spherical joint which allowed for slight misalignments between the two parts of the shaft, also enabled the turbine to be easily removed and was the work of Adrian Lombard and his small team. The arrangement, which was later to be generally referred to as the 'Lombard joint' or 'Lombard coupling', was the first major contribution which Adrian Lombard made on his own account to gas turbine technology and became a key feature of the new design and beyond.

After taking advice from specialist manufacturers, the Rover team decided to incorporate plain bearings to support the two-part compressor/turbine shaft. This design decision was later to cause difficulties and delay to the engine development programme, at a rather critical time for the Rover engineers.

However, the progress of the modified design, from drawing board to test bed, had been achieved in approximately nine months – a remarkable achievement on the part of the project team.

Although Whittle was aware of schemes which had been drawn up by the Rover engineers for a straight-through engine design, he was completely taken aback when he learned, in April 1942, that Rover had already made the first test run of such an engine at Waterloo Mill on 7 March, and, furthermore, that it had been sanctioned by one of the departments at the MAP some time previously, unbeknown to himself and other sections at the Ministry.

Such was the strength of feeling engendered by these developments that Frank Whittle himself headed a team from Power Jets which attended a special meeting in Clitheroe on 21 May 1942 to discuss the B26 engine. At the meeting it was decided that the Rover Company would be allowed to proceed with the B26 development, but that this would not be at the expense of the W2B production development.

The relationship between Whittle and the Rover Company now deteriorated further as a result of these events and reached the point where the two parties were hardly on speaking terms with each other. Whittle believed that Rover had lost interest in the W2B engine, and that this was not the time to make major design changes. He believed that the time factor for producing a reliable flight engine was crucial. He reasoned that all effort and resources should be being channelled towards bringing the W2B to a stage of development where it could be installed in the Meteor prototypes and tested in flight.

For their part, although continuing with the development of the W2B engine, Rover felt that whilst that design could eventually be brought to the production stage, their own B26 arrangement potentially offered great improvements over the earlier design and prepared a better path for future engine development.

CHAPTER 7

A TIME OF CHANGE

By early 1942, the Rover Company was experiencing considerable difficulties with the Whittle W2B development programme, and was under no illusions about the enormity of the task which had been undertaken. The original remit to develop the engine, and make it work reliably, was proving a very difficult goal to achieve.

The twin problems of engine surge and turbine blade failure dogged the development programme for many months. The surge problem was eventually overcome by reducing the number of vanes in the compressor and redesigning the diffuser, but, as described earlier, the difficulties related to turbine blade failures were not resolved satisfactorily until the new nickel-based alloys were satisfactorily developed. In early 1942, however, these solutions were still some way in the future.

As the months of 1942 passed, it became clear that there was no hope of delivering production engines from June of that year as had originally been envisaged.

The development programme with the W2B engine was considered by others, particularly Frank Whittle and some senior members at the MAP, to have slowed right down. This seemed to confirm Whittle's fear that Rover had lost interest in the engine.

A measure of the difficulties being experienced was indicated when, in April 1942, it was reported that only eight engines had been produced and that no prolonged endurance test runs had been made with the engine. This compared with the original MAP plan for Rover to deliver one pair of engines to Glosters for flight testing of aircraft and engines in March, followed by two more pairs in April.

The relatively small number of engines produced up to this time was understandable, considering the development difficulties which were being faced. There would have been little point in manufacturing large numbers of engines which could not meet requirements of performance, reliability and durability. Pressure started to mount however, for a speedier resolution of the problems.

For some time there had been a suggestion that a W2B engine should be flight tested in a special test aeroplane and so, during the latter half of 1942, a Wellington bomber was modified so that the jet engine could be mounted in the tail gun-turret position whilst retaining its twin propeller-driven engines for normal flight. The Rover-built W2B engine selected for the trials (unit SR 105) was despatched from Waterloo Mill on 16 July 1942. The installation of the W2B engine in the test aeroplane appears to have been carried out at the Vickers works at Weybridge where some twenty-five minutes ground running time was recorded with the tail-mounted engine.

The aircraft then transferred to the Rolls-Royce test unit at Hucknall where flight testing was to be carried out. Subsequent test flights were piloted by Rolls-Royce personnel with Rover Company staff taking charge of the jet engine for the in-flight tests. The W2B engine successfully completed over ten hours flying time at altitudes up to 20000 feet in August and September 1942 before being returned to Waterloo Mill. Following two short rating tests on the test beds, a strip inspection was carried out which indicated that the flame tubes were in good condition. Some of the stub pipes were found to have buckled but were considered to be capable of being rendered serviceable with repair.

Similar installations were later to be made in two other modified Wellington aircraft to enable further flight testing of engines to be carried out.

At about this time a new and serious development problem arose with a series of compressor impeller failures. Power Jets had two failures in September and a further one in October, whilst Rover had a similar failure in a W2B unit which they had on test.

John Swaine, who, as noted previously, was chief engine test engineer at

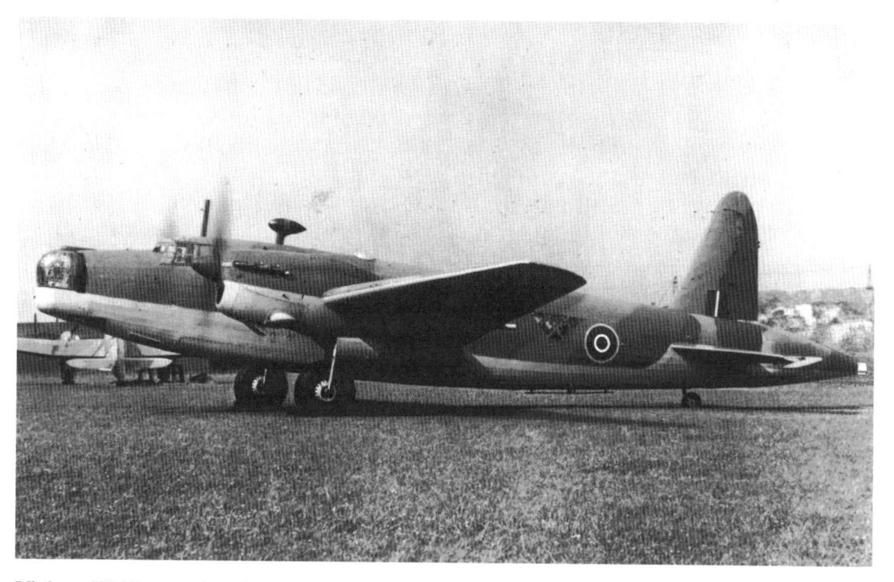

Vickers Wellington bombers converted to flying test-beds.
The first conversion with the W2B test engine fully cowled.

A later test aircraft with the cowls of the test engine removed for servicing. *(via Chaz Bowyer).*

Waterloo Mill, was at the controls in the test house at the time of the Waterloo impeller failure. Whilst attempting to reach 16000 rpm on rating test, the impeller suddenly burst. As was normal procedure at that time, two test fitters were inside the test-cell whilst the engine testing took place. During these early stages of testing, the occurrence of fuel system leaks were quite frequent but the front end of the engine, where most of the fuel system was located, could not be seen from the test cabin due to the position of the observation windows. It became necessary therefore, to have observers present during test runs.

The impeller failure caused the engine on test to split in two, and several segments of compressor casing flew over the men's heads to penetrate the inner walls of the test-cell causing damage. The two fitters were very fortunate to escape injury and luckily suffered nothing worse than a bad shaking.

The engine which failed in the Waterloo test house had run satisfactorily for a little under two and three quarter hours before the accident. Subsequent investigation revealed that the cause was an undetected flaw at the centre of the impeller which the inspection methods of the time had failed to find. Accidents of this nature led to instructions that personnel should not be allowed into the test cell during engine runs until after the engine had been

W2B unit destroyed on test.

run up to 16500 rpm. Indeed, a test rig had been built on the site early in 1942 to enable impellers to be run up to an agreed overspeed in a concrete lined pit as part of the inspection procedure. In this rig a close fitting casting surrounded the impeller under test, with the gap between impeller and casting being filled with hydrogen to limit the power required to rotate it to the required speed. The power source was a Bentley car engine driving through a reversed Ford rear gear to provide the necessary stepping-up ratio. This arrangement is said to have worked satisfactorily until the occasion when the hydrogen mixed with air in the pit and exploded lifting the concrete floor and cracking it.

Meanwhile, the testing of the prototype B26 straight-flow engine had provided valuable information to the Rover engineers. This 'proof-of-concept' unit had been designated STX by the Rover team – being the Straight-Through (flow) eXperimental engine. Construction of a second B26 engine, designated ST1, was completed in October 1942 and the unit was put on test at Waterloo Mill the following month. Early testing of this second engine revealed a problem of excessive oil leakage, particularly from the centre and turbine bearings. Considerable time had to be spent initially in trying to understand the reasons for the leakage and then in devising and incorporating modifications to overcome it. On the eighth test schedule, with the oil leakage problem contained if not yet fully solved, the engine was run up to 16500 rpm on its acceptance test. As 1942 drew towards its close a 10-hour endurance test was run, to be followed shortly afterwards by three 50-hour endurance tests.

Progress had also been made with the W2B engine. One of the W2B units had passed a 25-hour special category test at 1250 lb thrust, shortly to be followed by other 25-hour tests which were completed in December. By the following month a similar test of 1400 lb had also been successfully passed together with a 100-hour Type Approval Test at a rating of 1250 lb.

On 26 January 1943 a W2B engine of 1250 lb thrust was despatched to the Gloster Aircraft Company for installation in the recently completed second E28/39 experimental aeroplane. With the engine installed this aircraft was transported to Edgehill in Warwickshire towards the end of February in preparation for its maiden flight. Flown by test pilot John Grierson, the research aeroplane took to the air for the first time on 1 March 1943 and achieved a triple first. Not only was it the first flight of this particular aeroplane, it was also the pilot's first experience of jet flight and the very first occasion when any aircraft had flown powered solely by a Rover-built W2B gas turbine.

In the meantime two other W2B power units had been despatched to the Gloster Company in February for installation into one of the F9/40 (Meteor) prototypes in preparation for the aircraft's first flight. Initially rated at only 1250 lb thrust, these engines were destined not to be used for the aircraft's first flight. Higher powered engines were already on the test-beds and were producing marked increases in thrust within a very short time of these two engines being despatched. The two units were returned for modifications therefore, which allowed them to be uprated to 1600 lb thrust by May.

For some time prior to this, however, other events had been unfolding which were to have a far-reaching effect on this part of the gas turbine development programme. During 1942 the feeling of a need for fundamental change had been gathering pace in various quarters.

Earlier in the year Spencer Wilks had approached his friend Ernest Hives, (later Lord Hives of Duffield), who at that time was a Director of Rolls-Royce and held the position of General Manager of the Company, to suggest a possible link-up between Rover and Rolls-Royce on the Whittle W2B engine work and to seek guidance through the technical difficulties which the Rover team was facing.

In his response, Ernest Hives indicated to Spencer Wilks that he did not consider a link-up possible under the circumstances then prevailing. He did, however, arrange for Dr (later Sir) Stanley Hooker to make a number of visits to Waterloo Mill in order to examine the changes which the Rover engineers had made to the original Whittle design, and to advise on which of

The Rover-built W2B unit SR 110 ready for despatch for the maiden flight of the second E28/39 experimental aircraft. Note the heat-shield which was used with engines installed in the E28/39 aircraft.

these changes should be proceeded with. Since joining Rolls-Royce in 1938 Dr Hooker had risen to the position of Chief Assistant to the Chief Experimental Engineer and had built up considerable expertise on engine superchargers. It should perhaps be noted here that the supercharger on the Rolls-Royce Merlin piston engine and the compressor on the Whittle W2B gas turbine were essentially of the same configuration. The principal difference between the two lay in the Merlin supercharger having a single-sided impeller whilst the W2B compressor had a double-sided impeller. The expertise built up by Dr Hooker in this aspect of the work, together with his intimate knowledge of the Whittle engines arising from the liaison role which he had undertaken between Rolls-Royce and Power Jets, therefore placed him in a unique position which enabled him to make a full assessment of the situation at Waterloo Mill.

On reporting back to Ernest Hives Stanley Hooker observed that, in his opinion, the relationship between the two parties – the Wilks brothers and

Frank Whittle, had deteriorated beyond the stage where any reconciliationn was possible.

At a later meeting, held in September 1942 between the Wilks brothers and Ernest Hives, the Rover team again proposed collaboration with the gas turbine work then being undertaken. They made the point that Rover was fully occupied with getting the standard Whittle W2B engine right but that they firmly believed that work should be going ahead with a new design of engine with a thrust of 3500-4000 lb. They felt that they were not in a position to do this themselves but suggested that Rolls-Royce should take on this task and have full responsibility for the work. At the same time Spencer Wilks made it clear that Rover proposed to carry on with the testing and development of their B26 straight-flow design, although they considered it too small. He also indicated that Rover would be willing to let Rolls-Royce have one of the ST units to run at Derby. In the event, the main suggestions for this collaboration came to nothing as other events unfolded during the closing months of 1942.

The development of the Whittle engine appeared to some to have lost its momentum, particularly when measured against the original engine development programme. In addition, there seemed, at that time, no immediate prospect of a satisfactory flight engine, costs were mounting and the deterioration in relationships between the leading figures appeared to have passed the point of any possible return to normality.

Concern began to grow within the Ministry, particularly in those departments directly connected with the project which had themselves been responsible for setting out the policies from which some of the subsequent difficulties had arisen.

Frank Whittle had been pressing for the removal of the Rover Company from the project for some time, believing that they were incapable of the work and that they had lost interest in his W2B engine. He now began to suggest to the MAP that he should be allowed to become chief engineer of a new Power Jets/Rolls-Royce link up to produce his later W2/500 engine.

The MAP had been informed about the suggested involvement of Rolls-Royce in the production of the W2B engine. During the latter half of 1942, Spencer Wilks also advised Sir Wilfrid Freeman, Chief Executive of the MAP, that he felt that it would be wise and economical to reduce the suggested schedule of production until the specifications were more settled.

The background to the exploratory discussions which took place between Spencer Wilks and Ernest Hives at this time has never been fully revealed. It is known that the senior Rover management were concerned about retaining their previous position in the motor industry and wished to return to Coventry when circumstances permitted. It also seems probable that there was a belief that a future post-war government would impose a rationalisation of the British aero-engine industry and that the Rover Company would not be able to compete commercially with the established manufacturers. In addition, it had become clear, from the earlier contacts, that Rolls-Royce was now much more interested in the commercial future of the jet engine.

It has been said, by those who knew them well, that both Spencer Wilks and his brother Maurice were considered to be 'gentlemen' and were pleasant and generous-minded people who would have found the bad atmosphere which had developed between Rover and Power Jets alien and oppressive. Such an atmosphere would, no doubt, have encouraged a desire to be relieved of the jet engine work in which, it will be recalled, the company had originally become involved at the invitation of the Ministry.

During the latter half of 1942, Ernest Hives had made a number of visits to Waterloo Mill as a result of the earlier contacts by his friend Spencer Wilks, to see for himself how the work was progressing. The scene was now set, therefore, for new initiatives which might resolve the many difficulties which seemed to be besetting the jet engine development programme.

A full account of the moves leading up to the agreement, which resulted in the Rover Company withdrawing completely from the Whittle jet-engine development programme, has never been published. The initial steps may well have come from senior MAP officials and it is known that the changes had the support of the newly-appointed Minister – Sir Stafford Cripps. What is more certain however, is that Ernest Hives was a key figure in the negotiations and that it was his management of the situation which ensured that a smooth and effective exchange of facilities was achieved.

As mentioned previously, Rolls-Royce already had a contract from Power Jets to build and develop their own WR1 version of the Whittle W2B engine. Ernest Hives and his fellow directors appreciated the revolutionary role which the jet engine would have in the post-war period and had determined, some time before, that Rolls-Royce would play a leading role in the post-war manufacture of jet engines.

Events were subsequently set in motion which enabled Rolls-Royce to establish themselves amongst the leading international jet engine manufacturers, perhaps much more readily than even Ernest Hives might have dared to hope for.

It is interesting to note that, at this particular time, most of the leading figures – with the notable exception of Frank Whittle – regarded the jet engine only as a power source for high speed military aircraft. It was not generally appreciated that the advantageous power-to-weight ratio of the gas turbine would also make it eminently suitable for civil aircraft.

Amongst the wartime projects being undertaken by Rolls-Royce, work was being carried out on a new tank engine for the army. The design utilised a converted Rolls-Royce Merlin piston engine suitably adapted for its new role. The engine had been named Meteor but had no connection whatsoever with the aeroplane designed by the Gloster Company – the F9/40, with which it was to share a common name.

The tank engine project had probably experienced even more vicissitudes than the jet engine work. In September 1942, a committee of investigation set up by the Tank Board, had looked at the possibility of including Rover, together with a number of other companies, in the manufacture of the new tank engine, still under the design leadership of Rolls-Royce.

Ernest Hives saw that control of the design for the tank engine project, in addition to further involvement with production, could be an attractive prospect to an auto-motive company like Rover, particularly when viewed with longer term involvement in mind. He was also aware that Rover had several production factories which were nearing the end of contracts for manufacturing Cheetah aero-engine parts and knew they would be able to switch to the tank engine work, then being carried out at Rolls-Royce factories, relatively easily. His suggested solution, therefore, was a masterful and deceptively simple arrangement. Rover would hand over the jet engine work at Clitheroe and Barnoldswick to the Rolls-Royce Company, in exchange for which they would take over the control of the Meteor tank engine project.

One oft-quoted episode which took place towards the end of this chain of events, but which probably represents no more than the closing formalities, whereby the two senior figures involved completed the preparations for the handover which had been carefully prepared in the preceding weeks and months, is recounted by Stanley Hooker in his autobiography. He tells of travelling to Clitheroe with Ernest Hives one day towards the end of 1942 to have a meeting with Spencer Wilks. The three men had a meal at the Swan and Royal Hotel following which Hives turned to Spencer Wilks and said, "Why are you playing around with this jet engine? It's not in your line of business, you grub about on the ground, and I hear from Hooker that things are going from bad to worse with Whittle." Wilks reportedly replied, "We can't get on with the fellow at all, and I would like to be shot of the whole business." Hives then said, "I'll tell you what I will do. You give us this jet engine job, and I will give you our tank factory at Nottingham".

Stanley Hooker commented that, in as short a time as that the deal was done, but added that he believed that Hives had already got the necessary agreement of the Ministry. This most certainly must have been the case. The meeting had been preceded by a great deal of behind-the-scenes activity and arrangements had already been made to implement this course of action as speedily as possible.

The only Rover factories involved in the exchange arrangement were, of

The Swan and Royal Hotel Clitheroe, venue for the meeting between Spencer Wilks and Ernest Hives.

course, the two which were principally involved with the Whittle gas turbine work – Waterloo Mill in Clitheroe and Bankfield Shed in Barnoldswick. All other premises in their 'North West Group' were retained by Rover in order to continue the other war production which was being undertaken by the company.

In a memo dated 19 January 1943 Ernest Hives indicated that Rolls-Royce wanted the headquarters of their newly acquired 'Northern Factories' to be at Waterloo Mill, with all instructions to the Bankfield factory emanating from there.

A letter to Sir Wilfrid Freeman, written a few days later, gave further details of future plans when it was stated that the first problem which needed to be resolved was to change the character of the Barnoldswick factory from that of a production unit into a development and prototype production unit.

This latter course of action was implemented shortly afterwards when all of the experimental work was transferred from Waterloo Mill to Barnoldswick and the Bankfield works became an experimental and development centre. However, the earlier plans, involving Waterloo Mill, were subsequently altered and the Clitheroe works took on a different role.

A general acceptance of the need for secrecy and censorship during the war period possibly explains the fact that the exchange of facilities was received without question or surprise by the great majority of workers at Waterloo Mill and Bankfield. No official explanation was offered by the old or new managements and a considerable time was to pass before sufficient information became known to make the background to the action a little clearer.

The Rover Management Committee met at Chesford Grange on 4 February 1943 and Spencer Wilks reported that arrangements had been made for Rolls-Royce to take over the No 6 Factory. The actual date of transfer was expected to be about the end of March but personnel would only be withdrawn gradually as Rolls-Royce had asked Rover to assist them as far as possible until their own people were fully conversant with the work. A letter

MINISTRY OF AIRCRAFT PRODUCTION,

MILLBANK,

S.W.1.

24th January, 1943.

My dear Wilks,

Now that we are concentrating our efforts by a closer co-ordination of the work at Barnoldswick and Clitheroe with that of Rolls-Royce and Power Jets, it is an appropriate time to refer to the work which the Rover Company has done for us under the difficult conditions when they were more on their own. We here are appreciative of the work which your people, both in workshop and office, have done in the shadow organization of Waterloo Mill and Bankfield Shed. They set out at our direction on a programme of production which had to be cut back for reasons over which they had no control, and it is highly creditable that, despite the inevitable disappointment, they continued to work with enthusiasm and made a solid contribution to the advancement of this special work.

It may well be that some of them have felt from time to time that the number of engines they produced was incommensurate with their unceasing effort. They were, however, and are, working over new and difficult ground, and their contribution to the national effort is not one whit less than that of men and women who have the good fortune to see their work contributing to a satisfying flow of production.

Production in quantity of this special engine has yet to come, and I hope that your men, who by their pioneer work in this production field have brought it much nearer, will have the additional satisfaction of participating in it. This big advance in mechanical science is, from the operational point of view, only just round the corner, and if the folk at Clitheroe and Barnoldswick keep up the pressure, it should not be long before the corner is turned.

Yours sincerely,

(sgd.) W.R. FREEMAN.

Sir Wilfrid Freeman's letter to Spencer Wilks.

was read to the meeting from Sir Wilfrid Freeman following which it was recorded that – 'The Management Committee approved of the suggested transfer and noted with pleasure Sir Wilfrid's appreciation.'

At a further meeting on 4 March, the Rover Management Committee was informed that arrangements had been made whereby the handover of the management, and the formal transfer of administration, would take place on 31 March 1943. On that date, the Imprest Account would be transferred and Rolls-Royce would take over the entire control of Bankfield Shed, together with the administration and financial control of Waterloo Mill. At the Clitheroe site, however, it had been agreed that a small Rover staff would remain to carry out some work for Rolls-Royce, and, by arrangement with the Ministry of Supply, to do some work in connection with the Meteor (tank) engine.

Some aspects of the main work effectively began to be handed over before the official exchange date however. In a summary of the history of the Rolls-Royce involvement in the development programme from 1943, Dr Stanley Hooker, writing in 1945, commented –

> "Although we did not take over officially the responsibilities of the Rover Co Ltd at Clitheroe and Barnoldswick until 1 April 1943, we had in fact assumed responsibility at about the beginning of February that year."

The arrangements, whereby some of the Rover staff remained at Waterloo Mill for a short period beyond the official exchange date, meant that for John Swaine and some of his Rover colleagues, it was to be May or June before they finally left Clitheroe to return to the Midlands.

Before the transfer took place, however, senior personnel at both Waterloo Mill and Bankfield Shed were given the option of either remaining with Rover or transferring to Rolls-Royce. A number of the men and women chose to stay with Rover, particularly those who had previously worked for the company in Coventry, but the majority opted to transfer to Rolls-Royce and to remain with the jet engine work. Some of the Waterloo personnel who chose the latter course of action were Adrian Lombard, John Herriot, Jim Dening, Denis Drew, Sydney John Biker, David Ballantyne and J Sharpley Jones.

When asked by the Rolls-Royce team who they might recommend for the post of chief designer the Rover management had had no doubts or hesitation in suggesting Adrian Lombard's name. Accordingly, after interview, the post of Chief Designer, Rolls-Royce Northern Factories was offered to him and was readily accepted. To have reached this senior position in so important a company at the relatively early age of 28, as he had, was a magnificent achievement which reflected his great natural ability as a design engineer.

THE ROVER COMPANY LTD.

Acting for and on behalf of the Minister of Aircraft Production

BANKFIELD SHED,
BARNOLDSWICK.

WATERLOO MILL,
CLITHEROE.

By mutual agreement between the Minister of Aircraft Production and the respective Boards of the Rover Co. Ltd. and Rolls-Royce Ltd., an exchange of manufacturing facilities has been arranged between the two Companies.

As a result of this arrangement Rolls-Royce Ltd. (acting for and on behalf of the Minister of Aircraft Production) will assume responsibility for the management of the factories at the above addresses as from 1st April, 1943.

Unless notification is issued to the contrary, Rolls-Royce Ltd. will assume responsibility for the execution of all commitments properly incurred by the Rover Company Ltd., whilst acting in the capacity as Agents of the Minister of Aircraft Production in connection with the above factories.

Payment of any moneys owing to the Rover Co. Ltd., in connection with either of the above two factories should, after 31st March, 1943, be made to Rolls-Royce Ltd., at Bankfield Shed, Barnoldswick, and cheques, etc., should be made out accordingly.

For THE ROVER COMPANY LTD.,

Managing Director.

For ROLLS-ROYCE LIMITED,

Managing Director.

A letter issued by the Rover Company giving information about the exchange of manufacturing facilities. *(Author's collection).*

John Herriot, who had been appointed Development Engineer to the Rover Company in the previous September, now took on the role of Chief Test Engineer at Bankfield with Jim Dening as his assistant. Denis Drew was given the responsibility for the test-bed equipment with S J Biker as his assistant, whilst David Ballantyne was appointed as engineer in charge of the electrical and mechanical accessories on the engines.

Waterloo Mill was retained by Rolls-Royce under J Sharpley Jones but its function was to change. One consequence of this altered function was that many of the personnel at Clitheroe who opted to work for Rolls-Royce were transferred from Waterloo to Bankfield.

The stage which had been reached and the progress which had been made at Waterloo and Bankfield by the Rover Company up to the end of March 1943 may be summarised as follows:-

* Some thirty-two W2B engines had been produced.
* Over twenty W2B engines were being used on development work at Waterloo and Bankfield.
* A series of flight trials of the W2B engine had been carried out with various engines having been installed in the tail of the specially modified Wellington bomber.
* 100-hour Type Approval tests had been successfully completed for the W2B engine at a thrust rating of 1450 lb together with a 25-hour Special Category Type test at 1500 lb thrust rating.
* The second E28/39 research aeroplane had flown at the beginning of March powered by a Rover-built W2B engine rated at 1250 lb thrust. The aircraft had completed over 10 hours of flying during the month and the engine was about to be replaced by an uprated unit of 1450 lb thrust.
* Two W2B flight engines had been despatched to the Gloster Company in February for installation in a prototype F9/40 (Meteor) aeroplane in readiness for the aircraft's first flight.
* Four B26 straight-flow engines had been completed and were under test. The total running time for the four ST engines was a little under 362 hours.
* The first proof of concept straight-flow engine had completed 33 hours testing between March & November 1942.
* The second B26 engine, built in October 1942, had completed three 50-hour endurance tests during which a thrust of 1607 lb had been recorded
* A fifth B26 engine was under construction and nearing completion at Bankfield.
* The total running time for all types of engine by the Rover Company was some 1928 hours.

This then was the situation as the gas turbine programme was officially taken over by Rolls-Royce in April 1943. Although many of the difficulties which had presented themselves during the development programme had already been resolved, and others were well on the way to a solution, much work still remained before the engines were ready to be put into service.

The days when Waterloo Mill had been the principal engine development unit for one of the leading teams in the national gas turbine programme had now passed.

CHAPTER 8

CONTINUED ENGINE DEVELOPMENT BY ROLLS-ROYCE

In the re-organisation of the facilities at Clitheroe and Barnoldswick under Rolls-Royce, Dr Stanley Hooker took control as Chief Engineer. With Dr Hooker came a core of senior staff from Derby. These key personnel included :-

Christopher Ainsworth Davies	– assistant chief designer,
Fred Morley	– project designer,
Ron Kibbey	– head of detail design,
Harry Pearson	– performance development engineer,
Lindsay Dawson	– development engineer,
Geoffrey Fawn	– development engineer,
Robert Plumb	– mechanical development engineer,
Douglas Hall	– metallurgical laboratory,
Les Buckler	– works manager,
Les Saye	– assembly manager & assistant to Les Buckler,
Brian Guest	– PA to Les Buckler (& progress),
Henry Simons	– chief inspector.

The actual take-over was accomplished very smoothly and successfully. As individual senior Rover people departed, their places were filled by Rolls-Royce personnel. In the design office however, it was necessary to recruit experienced staff from outside to supplement those transferring from Rover.

Changes in management style were inevitable and caused mixed reactions amongst the workforce, probably reflecting personal experiences. For some, and particularly those involved in manufacture and assembly at Bankfield, the effect of the changes was considered 'sensational' as firm production schedules and targets were published, weekly production committee meetings set up under Les Buckler, and a range of additional plant obtained for the machine shop and tool room.

Looked at retrospectively, the new arrangements and the different approach of the management team were seen by some to have been important factors in the success which was later to be achieved by the Barnoldswick team under Stanley Hooker. Although the senior staff members transferring from Derby were relatively small in number, there were sufficient of them to create a Rolls-Royce 'air-minded' atmosphere, as Ernest Hives had intended. At the same time however, the geographical remoteness of Barnoldswick from Derby was considered an advantage as it prevented undue interference on a day-to-day basis.

One early consequence of the take-over of the Rover development programme was the decision by Rolls-Royce to halt work on their own WR1 engine in order to concentrate on the W2B engine. Pressure had been growing from the MAP over the preceding months for an all-out effort on the W2B development and the dropping of the ST project. The response to this pressure is reflected in the development testing records of the two engine types over the early months of 1943, as shown in the appendix.

The Rolls-Royce management decided that, as the W2B engine was virtually committed to production, major design changes were not deemed possible at that stage. The new development team therefore proceeded to develop the mechanical integrity of the W2B by applying their own engine testing approach. This had been established by Henry Royce in the early period of car manufacture and continued through to the piston engine development work on the Merlin, and beyond. The procedure consisted of running the engine for long periods, getting whatever thrust it would give, and thus establishing the reliability of the engine and all of its components before attempting to improve the engine's performance.

Building on the earlier developmental achievements of the Rover engineers, substantial increases were made both in reliability and the power

One of the prototype Gloster F9/40 jet aircraft (currently preserved in the Cosford Air & Space Museum). *(Author)*.

produced by the Whittle engine, and, in May 1943, a 100-hour test was successfully completed at the design rating of 1600 lb thrust. A few weeks later, on 12 June, one of the Meteor prototype aircraft flew with W2B engines, although, because of delays, another Meteor prototype had already flown with de Havilland Halford H1 engines on 5 March 1943.

The change-over of the project, from Rover to Rolls-Royce management, had met with the full approval of Frank Whittle. With the backing of senior MAP officials he now urged that Rolls-Royce should take on the production of his W2/500 engine whilst Power Jets would take responsibility for research and development of these, and other, centrifugal-type units. In addition, it was suggested that Rolls-Royce would have responsibility for preparing the W2/500 and later marks of engine to the type-test standard, for which they would be allowed to make any necessary design changes, provided those changes had Frank Whittle's agreement.

Whether Ernest Hives saw the seeds of potential future difficulties in these conditions, similar to those which had arisen between Power Jets and Rover, is not recorded. One can only speculate too on his views about Rolls-Royce playing a secondary role to Power Jets if these proposals went ahead. His initial assessment of the situation had already been revealed however when, in a note dated 28 December 1942, he had written :-

> "We want to make it clear that the mere fact of changing the management from Rovers to Rolls-Royce will not in itself produce the results. Rolls-Royce can only undertake this project on condition that they are allowed to operate it in a similar way to that in which they run their own business, and the management of the factory at Hillington for MAP. In other words, we must have complete control, subject to the technical policy laid down by MAP."

He had gone on to state :-

> "There is no intention of having a violent upheaval and change of staff at either Barnoldswick or Clitheroe. Mr Sidgreaves and I are going up there this week to have a look around, and we intend to follow it up next week with a technical meeting with Dr. Roxbee-Cox.
>
> "The first responsibility we shall assume is the technical responsibility, and in addition, to decide on what types and numbers of Turbines should be manufactured.
>
> "We do not blame Rovers for lack of success on the turbine project; we have every sympathy with their difficulties. Broadly speaking, there has been too much slide rule and not enough hardware.
>
> "We have got to face up to the fact that the Gloster (sic) F-940

machine is going to be disappointing, chiefly due to the fact that their original estimates were too optimistic."

The note had ended with the comment :-

"... we shall be disappointed if we cannot use the Rover organisation as it is."

Following a period of deliberation during which a complete assessment of the situation was made, the senior Rolls-Royce engineers concluded that, whilst the newer Whittle W2/500 and W2/700 designs promised greatly improved and more powerful engines, the straight-flow arrangement, developed by the Rover team at Waterloo Mill, represented a much better prospect for future engine development. The decision was made therefore, to use the Rover design as a prototype for their own engine development programme rather than to utilise the Whittle reverse-flow arrangement.

After making a number of changes to the B26 design – notably to enable a greater airflow which raised the design thrust to 2000 lb, the engine was produced by Rolls-Royce with the designation B37. The plain bearings of the B26 design were retained by Rolls-Royce, but this decision was said to have been 'bitterly regretted' later and alternative bearings were incorporated into subsequent designs as development of this basic B26-type of engine arrangement continued.

In June 1943, the first of the new B37 engines had its initial running-in test of some six and three quarter hours duration.

In keeping with Rolls-Royce policy, names were given to each engine design, and, in the case of the jet engines, it was thought appropriate to use the names of rivers to link with the concept of flow. Accordingly, the W2B/23, the designation of which had been shortened by Rolls-Royce to B23, was named the 'Welland' and the B37 became the 'Derwent'.

Eventually, as the 'Rolls-Royce B23 Welland', the Rover/Whittle reverse-flow engine was put into limited production at Barnoldswick. Some one hundred and forty development and production units of this design were ultimately produced by Rolls-Royce at Bankfield in addition to the thirty-two development engines of the same type produced by Rover. The engine went into RAF service in the summer of 1944 powering the Gloster Meteor F Mk 1 fighter which is particularly remembered for the destruction in flight of a number of the German V1 flying bombs.

Only a very short production run of twenty machines was completed for the Meteor F Mk 1 before a new version of the aircraft was produced. This was designated the F Mk 3 and was powered by two B37 Derwent engines. However, due to the fact that the newer engines were not immediately available, the first fifteen production aircraft of the later mark had to be fitted with Welland engines.

The Derwent I was put into production at a new Rolls-Royce factory which had been opened at Newcastle-under-Lyme, with John Herriot in charge of engine testing, and, from late 1944, the Derwent-engined Meteor F Mk 3 fighters entered RAF service. The Gloster Meteor, powered by its Rolls-Royce engines, thus has a significant historical claim to fame, being the only allied jet-propelled fighter to enter operational service during the Second World War.

The quest for improved and up-rated engines continued apace and Adrian Lombard and his design team produced the design for a new and more powerful engine which became the RB40. The 'R' prefix signified the Company's initial and was inserted as a result of a request made at about this time by the MAP, in a move designed to avoid confusion with established reference designations for bomber aircraft types.

As with the fighter aircraft referred to above, the British method of distinguishing progressive versions, or 'marks', of a particular bomber type of aircraft was to allocate the designations – 'B Mk 1', 'B Mk 2'..., often abbreviated to just 'B1','B2'....etc. In the case of the de Havilland Mosquito, a 'B35' version was produced towards the end of the war. The possibility of confusion and the need for a modified system for engine design codes can readily be appreciated therefore.

It is, perhaps, interesting to note that the origin of the 'RB' prefix to the engine type number was not appreciated by many and the letters were later commonly considered to represent 'Rolls-Barnoldswick'!

The RB40 engine, which was later to be developed into the RB41 Nene, rated at 5000 lb thrust, was the first totally new Rolls-Royce turbojet to be designed, built and tested, with all of the work being carried out at the Bankfield Works. To celebrate its success, Stanley Hooker invited Frank Whittle to visit Bankfield in November 1944 to see the engine running. Following the visit, a number of the key personnel and guests attended a dinner at the Swan and Royal Hotel Clitheroe, or, as it was rather facetiously referred to by some of the guests, 'The Swan and Jetpipe'!

During the course of the dinner the feeling of disappointment was expressed that there was no suitable aircraft at that time which would take the Nene engine, as it was too large for the Meteor. A suggestion was put forward, probably by John Herriot, that the engine might be scaled down to fit into the Meteor engine nacelle. This had not previously been considered and the question was immediately asked about the power of such a scaled-down engine.

Stanley Hooker suggests that Adrian Lombard did the design calculations there and then on the table cloth, although other accounts provide alternative

John Herriot, Air Commodore Frank Whittle and Dr Stanley Hooker – at Barnoldswick in November 1944.

locations and times. Whatever the circumstances, the calculation produced an answer of 3650 lb thrust. At that time the Derwent I engine was rated at only 2000 lb and so the prospect for the proposed engine was tremendously exciting.

Production went ahead and this new engine, exactly scaled down from the Nene by a factor of 0.855, became the Derwent V.

On 7 November 1945 two Meteor aircraft, with specially prepared Derwent V engines installed, took part in an attempt on the World Air Speed Record at Herne Bay in Kent. After each of the aircraft had made four runs over the course, it was announced that a new official World Air Speed Record of 606 mph had been established by one of the aircraft. The speed of the second machine was only marginally slower at 603 mph. The Clitheroe Advertiser of 14 December 1945 carried a short account of the celebratory dinner held at the Midland Hotel Manchester, which had been attended by representatives of the Rolls-Royce and Lucas Companies from Waterloo Mill.

The jet engine had progressed a long way from the first testing of Frank Whittle's WU experimental unit in 1937 and had finally 'come of age'.

THE AEROPLANE
Advertisements 16
JANUARY 4, 1946
A new world record
606 m.p.h
GLOSTER METEOR
(ROLLS ROYCE DERWENT ENGINES)
GLOSTER AIRCRAFT, BRANCH OF HAWKER SIDDELEY AIRCRAFT CO., LTD.

CHAPTER 9

ROLLS-ROYCE'S WORK AT WATERLOO MILL FROM 1943

A new building programme had been initiated for Waterloo Mill during the later stages of the Rover occupation. The open land on the Salthill side of the Waterloo Mill site, which had served as a football field for the Clitheroe Grammar School teams in the 1930s, was taken over for the new facilities. Soon after the Rolls-Royce take-over in 1943, workshop accommodation, referred to in more recent times as the 'Enterprise Works', together with the Type III engine test-house, were constructed and both buildings were brought fully into use during 1944.

The Type III test-house was designed to be an improved version of the earlier Type I test-house intended for performance testing. It contained four test cells, bringing the number of test cells on the Waterloo Mill site to eight.

From February/March 1943 a number of the departments which had been established by the Rover Company, including the design office and accounts section, were transferred to Barnoldswick, following which Waterloo Mill was designated as a 'Research Station' by Rolls-Royce under J Sharpley Jones. His assistant, for much of the next two years, was E Peregrine. It will be recalled that Sharpley Jones had been the performance specialist in the

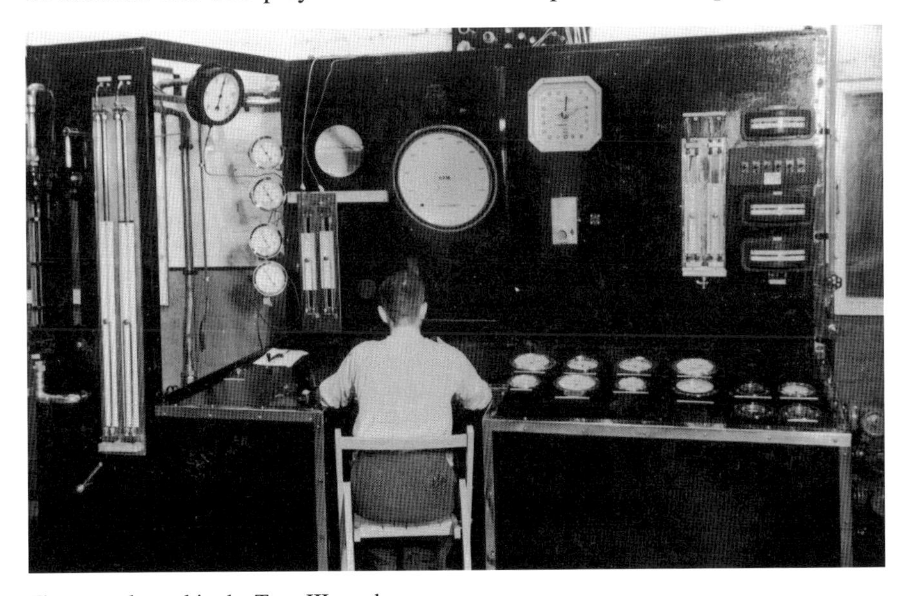

The control panel in the Type III test-house.

Water injection experiments on a Welland engine – circa November 1944.

original Rover team.

The work carried out at Waterloo Mill tended to be long-term research work for the company and ex-Bankfield staff have recalled that they came to consider the Clitheroe facility of that period as 'something of a backwater' – 'a place where people with wilder ideas could play about without getting in the way of the real work'!

Engines were frequently put on test in the Waterloo Test-Houses for the experimental programmes of both Rolls-Royce and Lucas, much to the annoyance of local residents who campaigned to have the tests stopped.

Company photographs which survive from this period and which carry captions linking them to the Waterloo test-beds, suggest that some of the research work carried out at Waterloo between 1943 and 1946 included:-

- Water injection experiments on a Welland, (Nov 1944).
- Tests using turbine traversing gear on the Rover B26 engine ST4, (Dec/Mar – 1944/45).
- Bifurcated jetpipes on a Welland, (Mar 1945).
- Tests with a dynamic brake attached to a Welland engine, (for early turboprop experiments), (Jul 1945).

- Variable jetpipe nozzles, (Sep 1945).
- Jet suction pump attachment to a Welland, (Sep 1945)
- Testing of the experimental RB60 engine, (Dec 1946).
- Tests using a plenum chamber ahead of the air intake, (Jan 1947).

The new workshop building had been completed some time previously but had been standing empty with only a skeleton staff of safety and maintenance personnel. It was then put into use by Rolls-Royce as a machine shop. Approximately thirty female machinists transferred to Waterloo Mill, possibly from the Newcastle-under-Lyme factory, to operate the milling machines which were installed as part of the manufacturing process for engine components. It has been suggested that this work, under Alf Stokes, involved the machining of blanks to produce guide vanes and/or turbine blades.

The personnel of the Research Department of Rolls-Royce at Waterloo Mill – circa 1945. The photograph is thought to have been taken when the department head, Mr J S Jones, was leaving to return to the Carrier Co. Back row (left to right) Frank Foreman, Ivan Charles McCoran Campbell, ? , Jim Snape, John Blakey, Rodney Hargreaves, Rio N Mirza, Jim Ratcliffe, ? , Horace Pye, Harold Hampshire, Gordon Paris (RAF), Bill Jordan, Bill Bracken. Centre row (left to right) George Collins, Tom Smith, Rama Reddy, Tom Dawson, Ted Smith, Jack Briggs, Tommy Grimshaw, Harry Pollard, Ned Smithies, Joe Green, John Christopher Holland, W F Robinson, E Peregrine. Front row (left to right) Bill Sanderson, Jack Taylor, Kathleen Black, Mary Leigh, J Sharpley Jones, Gwyneth Carter, Ann Mills, Frank Eccles, Harry Terry. *(via J C Pye).*

The Rolls-Royce Experimental Department personnel photographed in the control room of Test Bed number 5, Waterloo Mill – November 1946.
(Left to right) W F Robinson, Rio N Mirza, Tom Dawson, Frank Foreman, Billy Sanderson, Stanley Scott, Horace Pye, Mary Leigh, Albert Smith (??), Jack Briggs, George Collins, Tom Smith, ? , Joe Green, ? , John Blakey, Ted Smith, ? , Lance Bibby. *(via Mrs Mary Miller).*

At about the same time, an engine repair facility for Welland engines was established under the general control of the Bankfield Works Manager, Les Buckler. Carl Inglis was put in charge of the new facility at Clitheroe and built up the section from April/May 1944. It has been suggested that Waterloo Mill was chosen for this work partly because the engine test facilities were available on site, but also because, at that time, the Bankfield factory was being fully utilised for other aspects of the work. Over the 12 months or so of this first phase of engine repair work at Waterloo Mill, the section received development engines from Bankfield and flight engines direct from RAF units, for repair and refurbishment as they became time expired.

Eric Edmondson, who worked at Waterloo Mill as a fitter at this period, recalled that some of the Wellands which could not be refurbished for flight purposes were built up as instructional units for the RAF. He remembered meeting up with a number of these self-same units again some time later when he was based at various training establishments during RAF service.

The repair facility at Waterloo was transferred to one of the other Rolls-Royce sites in about August 1945, at which time the machine shop is also thought to have been re-located.

The work of the research station, which had continued through this period, also changed as the war in Europe approached its conclusion. During the earlier part of 1945 J Sharpley Jones transferred to Barnoldswick but, with the war then ended, he left Rolls-Royce later in the year to return to the Carrier Engineering Company, the firm from which he had been seconded to join the Rover team. His place at Waterloo Mill was taken by Rio N Mirza who was appointed manager of the section, which, over the next fifteen months or so of its existence, was referred to as the 'Experimental Section'.

At about the same time, part of the old Waterloo textile mill was partially de-requisitioned by the MAP and taken over by the firm of Lancaster Hosiery Company Limited, a subsidiary of the Middlebrook Manufacturing Company of Manchester, who had bought the premises at the beginning of the war. This company was to continue in occupation at the mill until it ceased trading in 1988.

A slightly later arrival, taking up accommodation in part of the old weaving shed in late 1948 after it had been vacated by the Rolls-Royce engine repair team, and causing the clatter of looms to reverberate around the building once again, was another subsidiary of Middlebrook Manufacturing, trading as Fir Tree Mills Limited. The firm produced woven textile goods for a number of years through the 1950s before production ended.

Engine repair work being carried out on Derwent engines at Waterloo Mill during 1947. Sub-assemblies bay.

Engine build section.

Engine despatch bay.

With the major part of the old Waterloo Mill being used for textile work once more, following the de-requisitioning of most of the original factory in 1945, the Rolls-Royce Experimental personnel moved to the 1941 extensions in the corner section of the old building, close to the factory tower, whilst continuing to utilise the various engine test-houses on the site. Engine testing was mostly carried out in the Type III test-house at this time with the older test-houses being utilised for rig testing.

The Experimental Section of Rolls-Royce, under Rio N Mirza, continued its work at Waterloo Mill until the end of 1946 when it closed and the workers dispersed, some transferring to other Rolls-Royce establishments.

Coinciding with this change, an engine repair facility was re-established once again, this time with Frank Griffin as manager. The task of this later repair section was to repair and refurbish Derwent I and Derwent V engines which the company had earlier supplied to the RAF. The Rolls-Royce and Lucas facilities at Waterloo Mill became a useful venue to which potential customers and visiting foreign delegations could be brought, particularly as the secret nature of much of the work at Barnoldswick made it a prohibited area for many of the visiting groups.

One such party, numbering about a dozen, was a Russian delegation which visited Clitheroe in October 1947. In these early post-war years the Russians were greatly interested in obtaining British turbojets and, some months prior to this visit, had been allowed to purchase thirty Derwent 5 engines and twenty-five Nene engines by the British Government – despite fierce objections from the Air Ministry. During their short stay in Clitheroe the delegation spent an evening as guests of the Council which, it was said, was much appreciated.

Towards the end of 1947 it was announced that Rolls-Royce would shortly be leaving Clitheroe. A letter from the company was presented at the meeting of the Town Council in November explaining that, owing to the curtailment of the general volume of their activities, the company found it necessary to vacate several of their smaller factories. The letter also expressed appreciation for the assistance given by the council and the town generally during their stay.

With the departure of Rolls-Royce in the early months of 1948, the newer workshop building became vacant – though not for too long. In September of the following year Major Atkinson transferred his business, which went under the title of Atkinson's Agricultural Appliance Company, from premises which the firm had previously occupied in Padiham and Burnley. Building extensions were started shortly afterwards.

Thus, from the early part of 1948, the Lucas company was the last of the three companies which had participated in the gas turbine development programme to remain at Waterloo Mill. They were to stay for another three decades utilising the site for a variety of purposes, but, with the departure of Rolls-Royce, the local population looked forward to an end to the sound of engine testing.

In the torchlight procession of 1948 held to mark the 800th Anniversary of the granting of Clitheroe's first Borough Charter, one of the floats depicted a 'fanciful reproduction of the Lancashire Witches and an up date version of the jet-propelled variety.' It was said in the Advertiser and Times report of 13 August that the motto carried on the float – 'Silence is Golden' – was cherished by all in the Salthill district. The rejoicing was, however, a little premature.

CHAPTER 10

THE WORK OF THE LUCAS COMPANY FROM 1942

To complete the account of wartime activities at Waterloo Mill, it is necessary to return to 1942 and to look at the work of the Lucas company once again, following the re-location of the experimental sheet-metal department to Burnley, as described earlier.

During the course of 1942, the Lucas management had decided that a small team of engineers should be formed at Waterloo Mill, to provide support and liaison between the main Lucas fuel-system development department and the Rover team. Once established, this team of engineers began to carry out experiments in its own right for Dr Watson, making use of the Rover engine-test facilities.

The Waterloo team of Lucas engineers was generally responsible to the main fuel-system development department at Birmingham and received authority and instructions from them, whilst maintaining a liaison with Dr Clarke, who had moved into the Wood Top works in Burnley with his staff in January 1943. Charles Bottoms, a development engineer from CAV, headed the team at this time. Another senior engineer who joined the team a little later was John Price. He was a servo-control specialist who had also worked for CAV and was later to take control of the unit when Charles Bottoms left Clitheroe.

A frequent visitor to the Lucas section at Waterloo over this period was a gifted Australian engineer named Richard J Ifield who had joined the Lucas Company in 1941. Some time earlier he had invented a multi-cylinder pump which was used by Dr Watson in the Lucas designed fuel-system. This type of pump subsequently bore the inventor's name, but, outside the group of engineers involved in the work, most people remember the family name through his son, Frank, who became the popular singing star of the 1960s.

The work carried out by the section at Waterloo Mill was mainly concerned with developing governors for fuel-systems and the effective control of fuel-systems at low speeds and low altitudes.

The design, manufacture and most of the development of new pieces of equipment was almost always done elsewhere. The components were then brought to Clitheroe for engine test when this was appropriate. Adjustments of the settings and the manufacture and incorporation of different valve profiles, lever ratios, diaphragm areas, spring rates, piston diameters, etc were introduced as the engine tests indicated that a better performance might result. Test rigs were used to initially determine optimum settings and adjustments for a given set of conditions, followed later by engine tests.

The Lucas Company developed electronic recording equipment

Front view of the Type III engine test-house – as it appeared following alterations to convert it for workshop accommodation. *(Author).*

Rear view of the Type III engine test-house. *(Author).*

incorporating cathode ray tubes, the light from which was used to draw lines on moving photographic paper. At one period, thought to be around early 1946, this apparatus was built into a Humber Super Snipe estate car (still camouflaged from its previous Service life), and was taken to Rolls-Royce and de Havilland on occasions for tests with newer engines which would not otherwise be readily available to the Lucas engineers.

The accommodation used by the fuel-system section was centred on the two-storey extension building of 1941. Test rigs were installed on the ground floor, alongside the garage for the Humber Estate, whilst a drawing office, general store and other offices were situated on the first floor. Other sections at that time included a machine shop and an area for welding and oxyacetylene brazing work.

During the period from 1943 to 1948, the Lucas team used the older test beds at Waterloo Mill for their fuel-system development work using Welland and Derwent engines, together with one of the Rover B26 engines – thought to have been unit ST3.

From the time of the departure of Rolls-Royce, early in 1948, only the newer Type III test beds close to the Mearley Brook were used for engine tests. Local people had hoped that engine testing might come to a halt with the departure of Rolls-Royce, but it was to be some years before their hopes were eventually realised. In the intervening period, the issue became a recurring theme on the agenda for the Borough Council meetings, and in letters to the local press.

Meanwhile, as sole residents on this part of the site, a rationalisation of the available accommodation was made by the Lucas team and the newer test house building was partially converted. The building was re-arranged to incorporate a laboratory, containing the half dozen or so test rigs, together with a drawing office and small workshop. Only one of the original four test cells was retained for the use of the fuel-system development team.

In the early 1950s, the senior Lucas management decided that the Clitheroe team should be situated much closer to the company's Shaftmoor Lane works in Birmingham, and so, in June 1952, a new facility was opened on a section of the ex-RAF airfield of Honiley, in Warwickshire. Here a purpose built test house was constructed and the new location was described as being a more elaborate replica of the old Clitheroe facility.

At its peak about forty people had been employed in the unit and it had become a small self-sufficient total experimental establishment. The number of employees had, however, reduced to about twenty-five by the time the decision was made to move to Honiley. This workforce comprised about eight qualified engineers supported by a small five-man machine shop, technical fitters, engine drivers, electronic recording operators, clerical and labouring staff. Of these about eleven people were re-housed and worked at

The personnel working for Messrs Joseph Lucas at Waterloo Mill – circa 1950.
Back row (left to right) Walter Scott, Bill Tremble, Jack Ashworth, Reg Porter, Fred Shears, Bert Jones, Frank Foreman, Mark French, Fred Harrison, Harold Yates, Ray Sharples, Hugh Hutchinson. Centre row (left to right) Jeff Gilbert, George Urry, Derek Seed, Walter Bell, Ken Barker, Geoffrey Coupe, Jim Moon. Front row (left to right) ? , Les Miller, Stella Fowler, Kelvin Shew, John Price, Betty Hall, Ken Haskins, Stanley Scott. *(via Mrs Greta Barker).*

the new Warwickshire site.

Following the departure of the fuel-systems team to Honiley, the rigs and other equipment were moved out of Waterloo and engine testing finally came to an end in Clitheroe when the one remaining test-bed was removed.

CHAPTER 11

FURTHER ACTIVITIES AT WATERLOO MILL

The Waterloo Mill site continued to be used by the Lucas company, though not initially in a production capacity. With only a small caretaking staff, it was first used for the storage of tools, plant, test equipment etc, from other sites. In the late 1950s Joseph Lucas-(Gas Turbine Equipment) Ltd set up a repair facility at Waterloo Mill, the purpose of which was to repair and/or refurbish those components of the engines which had originally been manufactured by the company.

The work was carried out on sub-contract, with the engines which were accepted for servicing being stripped at the Hillington (Glasgow) factory of the main contractor – Rolls-Royce. The Lucas engine components, which included flame tubes, exhaust nozzles and jet pipes, were then transported to Clitheroe by lorry.

At various times during this period of occupation by the Lucas Company, extra space was needed for storage and for workshop accommodation. In this post-war period, a suitable additional site was found in the old Carlton Mill

Inspecting a refurbished Avon jet-pipe at the Carlton Mill. *(via Jack Gregory).*

on Highfield Road in Clitheroe. During the war years, the mill had housed a section of the workforce of the Bristol Aeroplane Company attached to the main Bristol shadow factory at nearby Clayton-le-Moors. Complete Hercules radial aero-engines had been assembled here before being despatched for testing at the parent factory.

Engine modification kits for use by the Lucas team were now stored on this site. The initial stages in the repair sequence, which involved the stripping of jet pipes, exhausts, etc, were also carried out on the ground floor of the mill before the components were transported to Waterloo for repair/replacement work to be completed. Final re-assembly work was carried out at both sites over this period and on completion of the work, the units were returned to Rolls-Royce.

The Rolls-Royce engines which formed the basis for the refurbishment contract were mainly Darts, Avons and Conways. This work continued through into the 1970s, but at a much reduced scale in later years.

One form of the honeycomb fuel rod separators manufactured by Lucas for the AEA in the 1970s. *(Author).*

During this period, the buildings in use at Waterloo included the two-storey extension, previously used by the fuel systems team, and the Type III engine test house. With the engine testing equipment removed from the latter, as recorded earlier, the interior structure of the building was then altered again to accommodate further workshop space, offices and a canteen. The buildings tended to be loosely referred to by the workers as Firtree Mill, although this name strictly applied only to that part of the old weaving shed which had earlier been occupied by the weaving company of that name. This section of the old mill was subsequently used by the Lucas Company for some of the fitting and welding work on the engine components. Other activities which were carried out in the period up to the time when the Lucas company moved from the site in 1977, included work for the Atomic Energy Authority (AEA) and the explosive forming of components.

The AEA work involved the fabrication, by welding, of stainless steel honeycomb fuel-rod separators to very fine tolerances. An explosive forming facility, using a cordite charge detonated in a water pit, was specially constructed at the rear of the premises for the formation of components in titanium for the Ministry of Defence.

Changes in company policy led to the Lucas Aerospace Group making an announcement in November 1976, that the Waterloo Mill operations would shortly be transferred to Burnley, and that the site would then be vacated. At the time almost one hundred people worked for Lucas in Clitheroe, mainly men. During February 1977, all work involving the Lucas Company at the Waterloo Mill site was scheduled to cease but difficulties in the transfer resulted in the work continuing until later in the year when the company finally left the town. The final link with the gas turbine development work, which had been established in Clitheroe some thirty-six years previously, was thus severed. Jack Gregory who had been in the very first group of Lucas employees at Waterloo in 1941, retired as works superintendent with the closure of the site and, shortly afterwards, was awarded the Queen's Silver Jubilee Medal for his services to the aerospace industry.

Following the closure of the Lancaster Hosiery Company in 1988 due to difficult trading conditions, the decision was taken to demolish the original Waterloo Mill complex, including the two earlier engine test houses. This was completed by the spring of 1990 and a new housing development, to be later named Whittle Close, was constructed on the site.

In 1994, a decision was taken to demolish the Type III test-house building to provide car parking space for nearby businesses. At the time of writing, the only part of the wartime complex now remaining is the much altered and extended workshop building of 1943/44, now subdivided into small industrial units and known as Enterprise Works.

Of the original textile mill site, all that now remains is a part of the perimeter wall and the narrow roadway of Back Brook Street. Throughout most of the mill's history this route was the main approach from Waterloo Road and Taylor Street. It is still surfaced with the stone setts on which countless feet have trodden on the journey to and from the building which was once Waterloo Mill – or – as it was much better known by old Clitheronians – 'Th' Back Factory'.

(Author).

CHAPTER 12

AN ASSESSMENT OF THE ROVER COMPANY'S CONTRIBUTION TO EARLY GAS TURBINE DEVELOPMENT

Honour and acclaim have rightly been accorded to Sir Frank Whittle for his pioneering role in harnessing the gas turbine as a power plant for flight – a revolutionary development which has had as dramatic and important an impact on air transport as the introduction of steam power to water-born transport in an earlier era. But what conclusions might fairly be drawn on the contribution of the Rover Company's engineers to the ultimate success of the project?

A balanced and equitable assessment of the activities of the Rover Jet Engineering Team in the period up to March 1943 is not an easy task. The achievements of that period tend to be over-shadowed by a number of associated factors, all tending to either unduly highlight the difficulties – which undeniably occurred, or to mask the progress made.

Such factors include:-

- the breakdown in personal relations which occurred between Sir Frank Whittle and the Wilks brothers;
- a lack of clear resolve at the beginning of the programme on the part of the Air Ministry;
- a much lengthier development phase for the W2B engine than had been envisaged, due, in part, to questionable planning decisions and unrealistic targets initially set by the Air Ministry;
- difficulties in the development programme which arose through working at, and beyond, the very boundaries of technical and scientific knowledge of the time;
- transfer of control over the project to the Rolls-Royce Company at a time when significant progress had been recently achieved;
- subsequent successes enjoyed by the Rolls-Royce team as they continued the work on the project.

If one were to attempt to make an assessment solely on the original objective of developing the W2B engine to the flight testing stage and the preparation for quantity production, then the conclusion would have to be that this objective was quite obviously not realised before the exchange of 1943. This would, however, be a very narrow set of criteria on which judgement might be made. Nor is it fair to make a direct comparison between the progress made before the transfer of control at the beginning of April 1943, at a time when some of the more fundamental problems were rapidly being overcome, or were becoming more fully understood, and the progress made later when a number of aspects of the new advanced technologies had been further developed and improved.

Reference has already been made to the length of time taken to bring the W2B design to the production stage, an aspect seized upon by some writers in their criticisms of the Rover engineers. Such writers give the impression, by implication, that the team under Maurice Wilks was the only one actively involved in the W2B engine's development. In reality, as has already been noted, no single company or organisation could possibly have undertaken all of the research and development work which was required at that time. Many groups were actively engaged in the search for solutions to the numerous technical problems which arose. Indeed, tribute to these other teams has often been lacking in the past, despite the substantial contributions which they provided towards the ultimate success of the project. Two significant participants have been briefly mentioned in this study, viz – Messrs Joseph Lucas with their work on the development of combustion and fuel systems, and the metallurgists, in companies such as Henry Wiggins, with their development work on the new materials which were able to withstand the extreme physical conditions within the gas turbine.

It was to be late in 1942 before the specialist firms managed to successfully produce, test and develop the new materials, such as Nimonic 80, to the stage where they could be reliably utilised. These new alloys enabled turbine blades and other components to be incorporated into the engines with the necessary properties which then enabled prolonged engine running to take place.

A frequently overlooked aspect of engineering development of this nature is that progress often depends upon research on a broad front. It is not always appreciated that when advances in engineering design requirements demand new technology, the production manufacturers may also be required to create and develop new materials, new types of tools to cut and form those materials, and new construction techniques. Each can be a time-consuming process.

It is interesting to read the comments made by John Grierson, a senior test pilot with the Gloster Company who flew both the E28 and F9/40 aircraft. Writing in 1945 and recalling the development problems with the W2B engine, he wrote – 'When the first development engines were run, they were found to suffer from several troubles which would render them unfit for flying, so that considerable improvement was urgently necessary. The two major snags were surge and failure of turbine blades. Serious surging was eliminated after a few months work, but until a new material could be found, turbine blade failures persisted ... Not until July 1942 did a satisfactory blade material in the form of a few sets of blades from America become available, and at the end of the year an even better alloy was being produced for the purpose in this country.'

John Grierson's further assessment of the W2B engine is also of interest. He commented – 'No one could pretend that this was a brilliant engine, but it worked ... Even at the moment when the first B23 flew in the E28, the engine was really obsolete, in that better engines were already running on the bench ... One by one the initial weaknesses of the B23 were weeded out through the lessons of flight testing ... [and] ... many months of patient research was necessary ... It can fairly be said that the Rolls-Royce B23 was the best stabilizing factor in British jet propulsion work whilst engines of higher power and efficiency were being perfected.'

Contemporary records indicate that many of the basic problems which arose during the development of the W2B engine, were well on the way to being resolved by April 1943 when the programme was handed over to Rolls-Royce. The early successes of Rolls-Royce with their B23 (and B37) engines emphasise the continuous nature of the programme of development which took place, albeit with important additional resources and a new senior management with acknowledged expertise in aero-engine work.

It is unfortunate that a number of the authors who have previously written accounts covering the activities being reviewed here, have quoted stages in the development of the W2B engine out of context. Such accounts have consequently lost sight of the continuity of the work over the changeover period in the first half of 1943. One example, which has often been used, reports the successful 100-hour type-tests on the W2B engine at 1600 lb thrust rating in April and May 1943 (ie in the two months following the official date of the Rover/Rolls-Royce changeover). The selection and emphasis of this single phase in the development programme probably reflects the fact that these tests were carried out at the engine's full original design thrust. The success of this part of the test programme is rightly seen as a milestone, but ignores similar successful 100-hour type-approval tests at 1250 lb thrust in the previous January and a 100-hour type-approval test at 1450 lb rating in March. Misinterpretation of the facts can therefore easily ensue.

The comments of one of the leading figures involved in the project at that time reveal the opinions of a greatly respected engineer who had intimate knowledge of the work carried out by the Rover team. Commenting in 1994, Harry Pearson – the senior Rolls-Royce performance development engineer at Barnoldswick from 1943 under Dr Hooker, said – 'Rover had made a good contribution [to the development programme] under very difficult circumstances. They had had problems, but most of them were being solved by the time we got there. There had certainly been a lot of bugs on the B23 which needed to be got out and, although Rover lacked 'airmindedness', they had done a good job.'

An assessment of the Rover team's work on the Whittle W2B engine is then, one of a qualified measure of success. The development programme progressed, steadily overcoming a multitude of design, development and research problems which arose, and subsequently prepared the way for further development by the Rolls-Royce team under Dr. Hooker. That the ultimate goal, of getting the reverse-flow engine into an operational aircraft, was not finally accomplished until some time after the programme had been handed over to the Rolls-Royce Company, should not detract from the Rover Company's achievement.

It is appropriate and necessary, in drawing up this assessment, to consider separately the work carried out by Rover on their straight-flow B26/ST design. Here, the views of Dr E A Watson, Chief Engineer of Joseph Lucas and Company, are relevant. Speaking after the war and referring to the Rover Company he said, 'I regret to say their efforts were strenuously opposed by the official parties, Whittle, Hawthorne and the RAE, and it is a matter of great credit to Rover's that, despite official cold shouldering, the B26 engine was built and running by the autumn of 1942'.This statement, made by an eminent and widely respected engineer who had worked alongside the Rover engineers, points towards the most important aspect of the work of the team under the leadership of Maurice Wilks.

The new straight-flow engine progressed from initial drawing board layout to test bed running in a period of a little over nine months. Despite fierce opposition, the engine was developed by the Rover engineers to the stage where four engine units had been put on test before the official exchange date of 1 April 1943, and three 50-hour endurance tests had been successfully completed in January and February of that year. With some design changes, the Rover engine was selected by Rolls-Royce to become the prototype for their own development – the B37 Derwent. (This, in spite of other advanced designs of the basic Whittle reversed-flow engine being available to them.) In its turn the B37 design led to a succession of highly successful Rolls-Royce aero-engines in the early post-war years, which paved the way for the company to establish itself as a world leader in gas turbine design and production.

Great courage and vision had been displayed by Spencer and Maurice Wilks whilst facing sustained and determined opposition to their improved engine arrangement between 1941 and 1943. This aspect of the Jet Engineering Team's work is surely the one for which particular credit should be given. The development of the B26 engine was a major achievement which should receive due recognition, and one for which the period of occupancy at Waterloo Mill by the Rover team should be especially remembered.

APPENDICES

A A Chronology of some of the events outlined in this study.

B A Map showing the location of places referred to in the text.

C Layout of the Waterloo Mill site.

A plan showing the extended Waterloo Mill site circa 1945.
A sketch plan of the old Waterloo Mill buildings.

D Engine test arrangements at Waterloo Mill.

The Waterloo Mill engine test-houses.
Plan showing the location of the engine test-houses.
Table comparing features of the three types of test-house.
Sketch and plan of the Type I test-house.
Plan showing the Type III test-house.

E The Rover-designed W2B/26 Straight-Flow engine.

Engine design details and performance.
The B26 units STX to ST4.

F Engine testing from 1941 to 1943.

The Rover Company's engine testing up to 31 May 1942.
Engine testing from mid-1942 to 31 May 1943.

APPENDIX A

A CHRONOLOGY OF SOME OF THE EVENTS OUTLINED IN THIS STUDY

Jan 1930	Frank Whittle first applies for patents for his revolutionary gas-turbine engine design.
Mar 1936	The firm of Power Jets is incorporated.
12 Apr 1937	The first run of the Whittle experimental engine (the WU) takes place at the BTH works in Rugby.
Mar-Apr 1940	The Air Ministry decides to offer direct contracts to the Rover Company for development & production Whittle engines. Rover decides to subcontract the combustion and fuel system work to Lucas.
Oct 1940	Waterloo Mill is earmarked for the gas turbine development work of Rover and Lucas.
14 Nov 1940	Coventry is heavily bombed by German aircraft.
Mar-Apr 1941	The first of the Lucas and Rover workers begin to arrive at Waterloo Mill.
15 May 1941	The first flight of a British jet-powered aircraft takes place at the RAF airfield of Cranwell. The E28/39 research aircraft is powered by a single Whittle W1 engine.
Apr/May 1941	A Rover-built W2 engine is tested by Power Jets.
31 Oct 1941	Engine testing begins at Power Jets on the first W2B engine supplied by the Rover Company. The second unit is first tested at Clitheroe on 27 Nov.
late 1941	Permission is given by the MAP for the Rover design team at Waterloo to produce an alternative straight-through (ST) design of engine.
Dec 1941	The Lucas experimental sheet metal section move from Waterloo Mill to Burnley.

7 Mar 1942	The STX engine has its first run on the Type I testbeds at Waterloo.
21 May 1942	Frank Whittle heads a Power Jet delegation to Clitheroe to discuss the ST engine – officially referred to as the W2B/26. Rover are allowed to continue provided it does not affect the development of the reverse-flow W2B engine.
Aug-Sep 1942	A Rover built W2B engine is tested in the air for the first time in the tail of a specially converted Wellington bomber.
Dec 1942	Agreement is reached for Rolls-Royce to take over the jet engine development work from Rover in exchange for Meteor tank engine production. The decision is taken by Ernest Hives that all experimental and development work will be transferred from Waterloo Mill to Barnoldswick.
Late 1942	Lucas decided to set up a fuel-system development team at Waterloo Mill.
1 Mar 1943	The second E28/39 aircraft flies for the first time powered by a Rover-built W2B engine.
1 Apr 1943	The official handover date between Rover and Rolls-Royce. Waterloo Mill becomes a Research Station for Rolls-Royce under J Sharpley Jones.
May 1943	A 100-hour test of the W2B is successfully completed by Rolls-Royce at its design rating of 1600 lb thrust.
12 Jun 1943	One of the prototype Gloster F9/40 (Meteor) aircraft flies with W2B engines.
Nov 1944	Frank Whittle and others attend a celebratory meal at the Swan & Royal Hotel in Clitheroe following the successful tests with the new Nene engine.
1945	Waterloo Mill becomes an Experimental Station for Rolls-Royce under R N Mirza.

7 Nov 1945	A Gloster Meteor aircraft, powered by two RR Derwent V engines, captures the absolute World Speed Record at 606 mph.
Dec 1946 – Jan 1947	The Experimental section at Waterloo Mill closes and Rolls-Royce set up an engine repair unit.
Nov 1947	Rolls-Royce give notice that they intend to leave Clitheroe in early 1948.
May 1952	The Lucas Fuel System team leave Waterloo and transfer to Honiley in Warwickshire. The company retains a presence at Waterloo.
c. Jul 1977	The Lucas Company transfer their production work from Waterloo Mill to Burnley, thus ending their thirty-six year association with the town.
Sep 1988	The Lancaster Hosiery Company ceases production at Waterloo Mill and a subsequent decision is taken to re-develop the site.
Feb-Mar 1990	The Waterloo Mill site is completely cleared following which a new housing development is commenced – later to be named Whittle Close.

APPENDIX B

A MAP SHOWING THE LOCATIONS OF PLACES REFERRED TO IN THE TEXT

1 – Glasgow (& Hillington)
2 – Lancaster
3 – Blackburn
4 – Manchester
5 – Chester
6 – Newcastle under Lyme
7 – Derby
8 – Hucknall
9 – Nottingham
10 – RAF Cranwell
11 – Grimsby
12 – RAF Cosford
13 – Birmingham (& Tyseley)
14 – RAF Honiley
15 – Coventry
16 – Rugby
17 – Lutterworth
18 – Weybridge
19 – London
20 – Herne Bay

Clitheroe
Barnoldswick
W – Waddington
Gr – Grindleton
Sa – Sawley
C – Chatburn
D – Downham
R – Rimington
G – Gisburn
B – Bracewell
E – Earby
Ca – Carleton
S – Skipton
CM – Clayton le Moors
P – Padiham
Accrington
Burnley

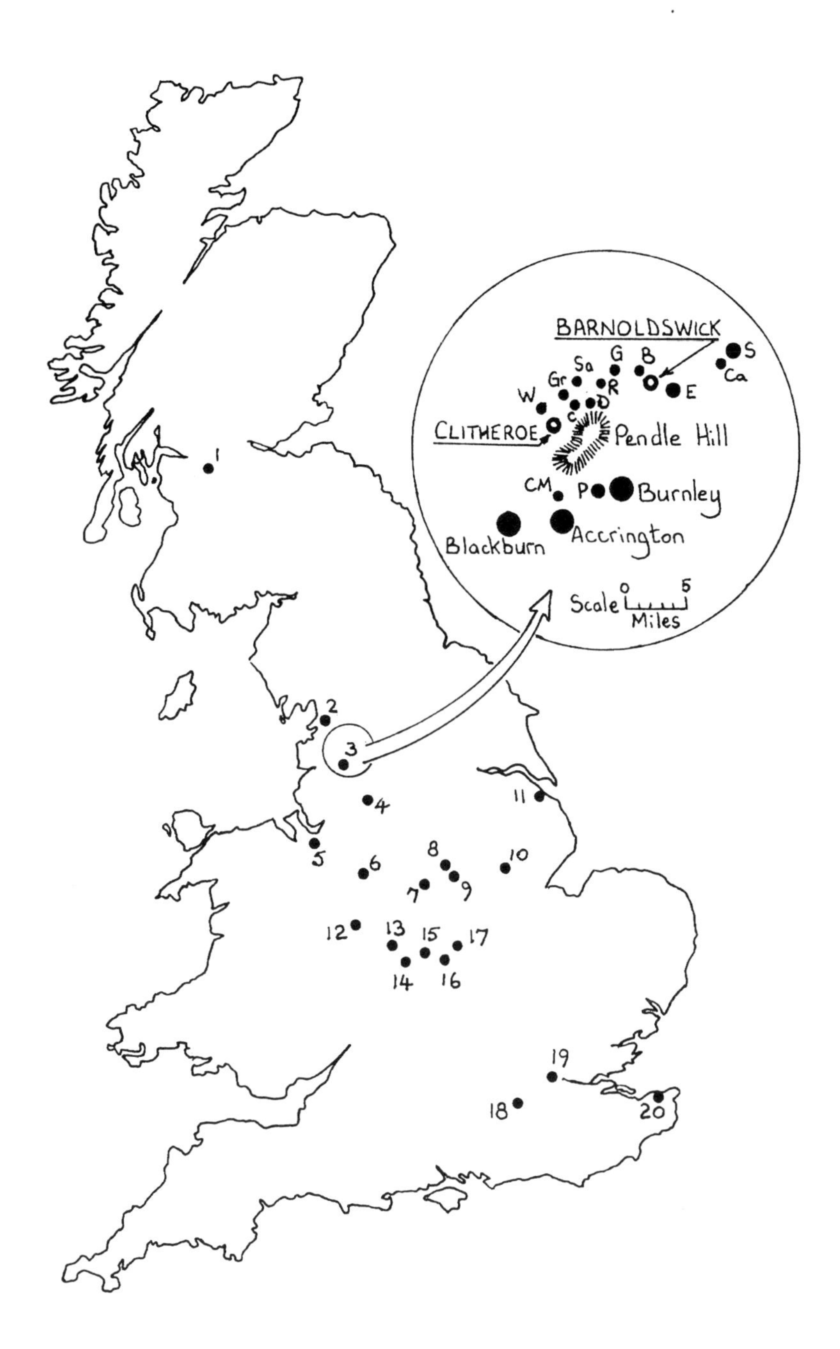
BARNOLDSWICK
S
Ca
G
B
Sa
Gr
R
E
W
D
C
CLITHEROE
Pendle Hill
CM
P
Burnley
Blackburn
Accrington
Scale 0 5
Miles
1
2
3
4
5
6
7
8
9
10
11
12
13
14
15
16
17
18
19
20

APPENDIX C

A PLAN SHOWING THE EXTENDED WATERLOO MILL SITE (circa 1945) PRIOR TO DE-REQUISITIONING

KEY :-

1. The original Waterloo textile mill (built 1858).
2. Back Brook Street entrance into the mill yard.
3. Cottages in Back Brook Street.
4. The Mearley Brook and footbridge.
5. Office and workshop extension of 1941.
6. Type I test house of 1941 (test beds 1 & 2).
7. Canteen.
8. Bicycle sheds.
9. Unidentified
10. Type II test house of 1942 (test beds 3 & 4).
11. Paraffin tanks.
12. Salthill View entrance to extended site.(1942?)
13. Kendal Street entrance to new workshops and offices.
14. New gatehouse.
15. New office/workshop accommodation of 1943-44.
16. Type III test house of 1943-44 (test beds 5, 6, 7 & 8).
17. Impeller test house.
18. Telephone Switchboard – (later sited in the Kendal Street gatehouse).
19. Fire Station (circa 1941-43).
20. Air-raid shelters.

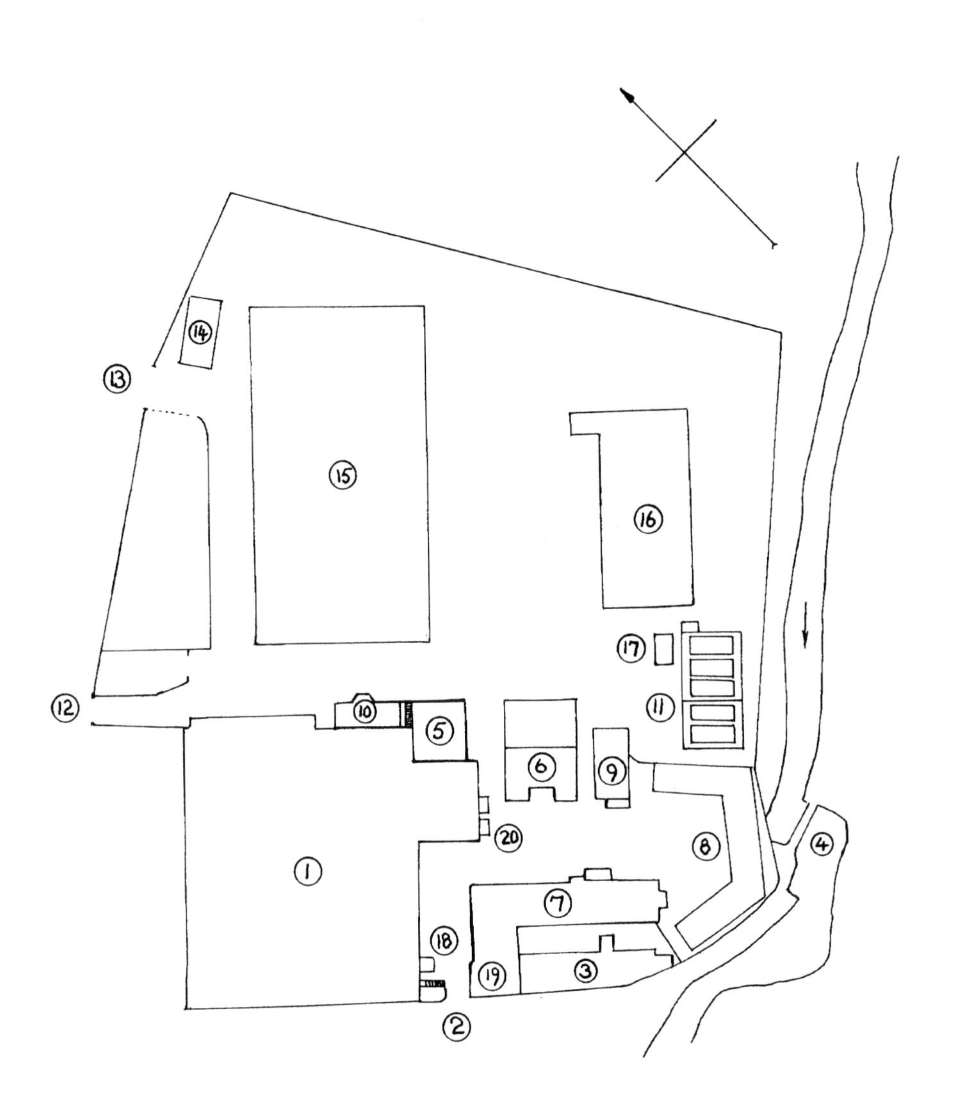
13
14
15
16
17
11
12
10
5
6
9
8
4
20
1
7
18
19
3
2

APPENDIX C

A SKETCH PLAN OF THE OLD WATERLOO MILL COMPLEX – BASED ON THE ARRANGEMENT IMMEDIATELY BEFORE DEMOLITION (circa 1989-90)

KEY :-

1. Single-storey weaving shed of 10 bays with northern-light roofing.
2. Two-storey stone-built building with pitched roof, believed to have been originally used for warping and winding departments and as a warehouse.
3. Flat-roofed section above original mill-engine room. Large cast-iron water tank situated on roof.
4. Stone-built, two-storey building with flat roof. Original boiler room situated at ground level. (Photographs, dating from about the turn of the century, suggest that this section of the factory originally had an additional storey and a pitched roof.)
5. Brick-built, square-section factory chimney.
6. Stone-built water tower.
7. Low two-storey building – part of the extensions of 1941.
8. Single-storey, brick-built extension with high external doorways – this section was originally built in 1942 as the Type II engine test-house.

9/10. Two small, box-like, brick-built structures with concrete roofs, windowless but having external access doors – erected on the roofs of buildings (4) and (8) – thought to have been constructed to house part of the fuel supply/control system for the engine test-houses (circa 1941/2).

11. Main entrance to the mill site from Back Brook Street.
12. Brick-built, single-storey extension constructed after the war when part of the factory had reverted to textile production.
13. The Type I engine test-house facility constructed in 1941.
14. Pill-box overlooking Back Brook Street, erected on the corner of the weaving shed roof for wartime defence purposes.
15. Single-storey building, constructed circa 1941 and used as a canteen during the war-time period.

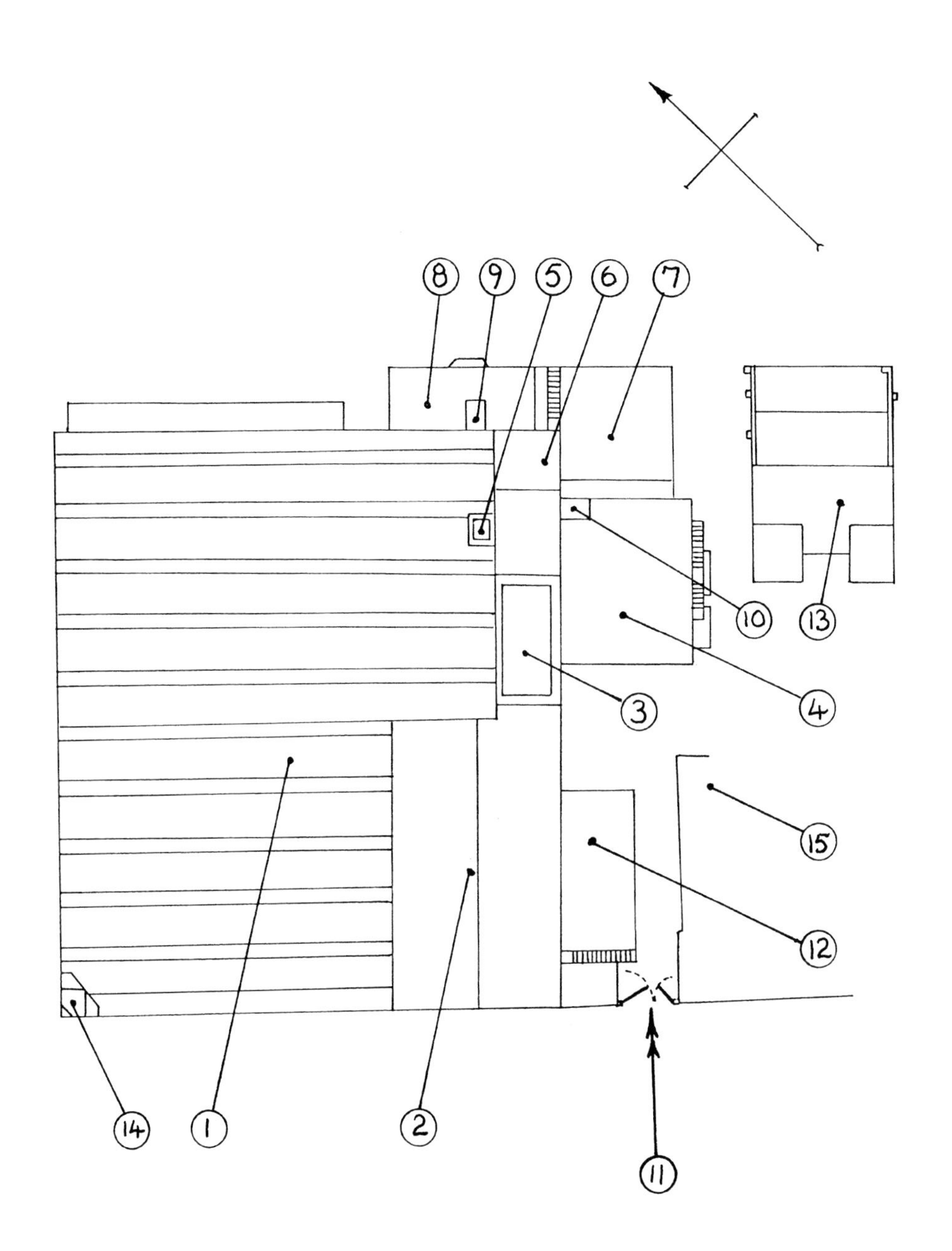
8
9
5
6
7
10
13
3
4
15
12
14
1
2
11

APPENDIX D

THE WATERLOO MILL ENGINE TEST-HOUSES

The three test-house buildings constructed at Waterloo Mill between 1941 and 1944 were generally similar in layout although each type had different test bed and air intake arrangements. The instrumentation incorporated into the different 'types' of test house varied somewhat according to the specific purpose for which they were intended. In each of the three designs the control rooms were centrally located between twin test cells and were orientated in the same way as the test cells which they served.

a) Type I test-house.
   Construction was begun on this unit before the site was occupied by the Rover personnel. An unusual feature of this design was the arrangement of the test stand being mounted on a raft floating on water. This was an early attempt to reduce friction when measuring engine thrust. Inclined steel plates were erected in the enclosed yard to the rear of the test house to deflect the jet streams upwards. A glass window, protected by a steel shutter when not in use, was provided in each deflector to enable an observer to look up the jet pipe, with the engine running, to check for combustion irregularities.

b) Type II test-house.
   The method of mounting the engine test stands, utilising a pivoted frame, was completely different to that used in the earlier design. Considerable development was necessary before this arrangement was considered satisfactory, the main difficulties being hysteresis in the sac unit and inconsistency of the gauge unit. With the construction of the new facilities in 1943-44, the two test cells in this section were allocated for engine testing by the Lucas fuel-system development team, and later still were utilised by them for rig testing.

c) Type III test-house.
   The original drawings for this building show that space was allowed for a further two test cells and associated control room at the north-eastern end of the building. These were not built - presumably due to the changed function of the site after the Rover/Rolls-Royce exchange in 1943. The air-intake and interior arrangements of this building were considerably altered when the Lucas Company's Fuel Control Section took over this part of the site in 1948. From then until 1952 only a single test cell was retained. At the latter date, when the group left the site, the one remaining test-bed was taken out.

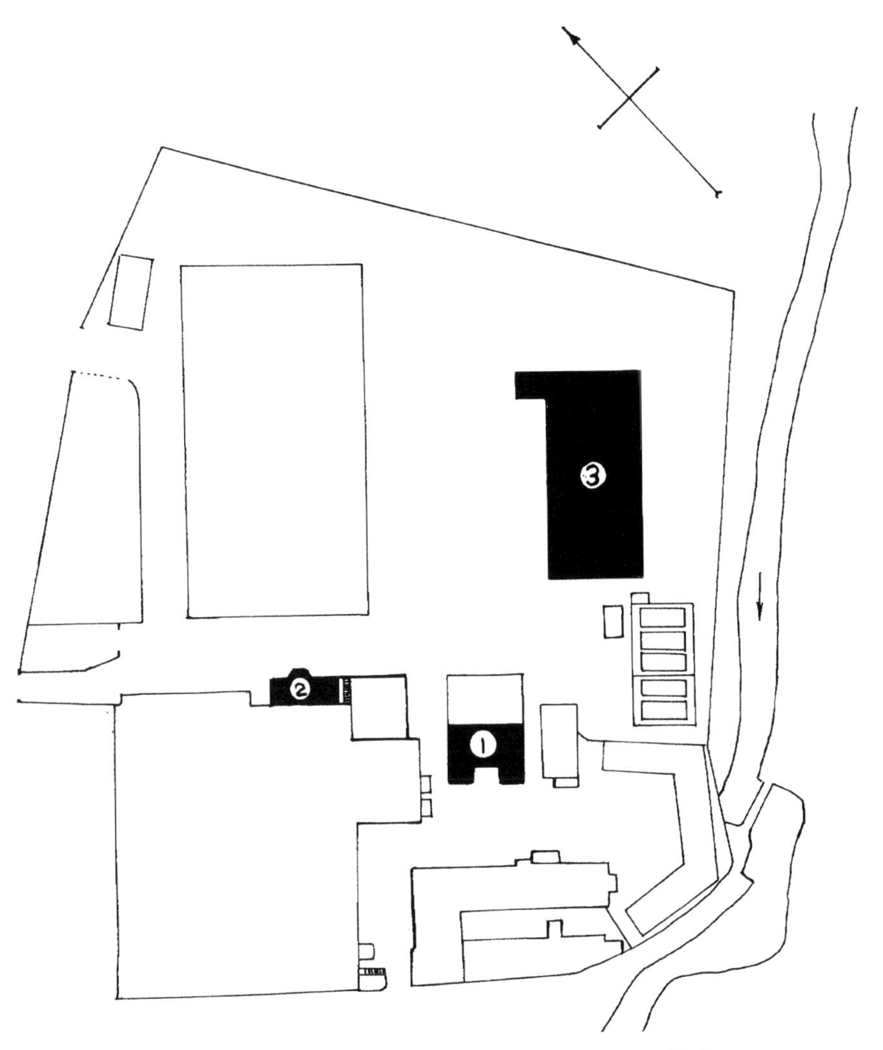

Plan showing the location of the engine test houses on the Waterloo Mill site.

KEY :-

1 Type I test house containing testbeds 1 and 2 – built 1941.
2 Type II test house containing testbeds 3 and 4 – built 1942.
3 Type III test house containing testbeds 5, 6, 7 and 8 – built 1943-44.

APPENDIX D

A TABLE COMPARING THE FEATURES OF THE THREE TYPES OF ENGINE TEST-HOUSE AT WATERLOO MILL

	Purpose	Test Cells	Control Room(s)
TYPE I (1941)	Intended primarily for performance testing.	Two cells – one on each side of control room. Each test cell measured 24′L x 14½′W x 13½′H.	Centrally located between twin test cells. Operator sat sideways-on to test cell window.
TYPE II (1942)	Simpler than the Type I test house. Intended primarily for endurance testing etc.	Two cells – one on each side of control room. Smaller than Type I units.	Centrally located between twin test cells. Operator sat facing test window.
TYPE III (1943-44)	Intended as an improved version of the Type I test houses.	Four cells arranged in line with two control rooms – each serving a pair of test cells.Each cell measured 27¼′L x 18′W x 18′H.	Two control rooms – each serving two test cells. Operator sat facing test window.

Air Intakes	Test Stand Mounting	Thrust Measurement
Twin intake towers on roof of test house facing rearwards. [Additional intakes on outer sides of each test cell later dispensed with].	Test stand mounted upon a raft floating on water. Lateral movement restrained by ball bearing rollers on a horizontal guide rail at floor level above raft with a torque arm between top of stand and test cell sidewall.	Thrust transmitted via levers to an Avery weighing machine. By the use of dead weights and adjustable lever ratios thrusts up to 3600 lb could be measured.
Intakes arranged high up in the side walls opposite control room..	Test stand carried on vertical legs pivoted top and bottom by antifrictional bearings in fore and aft directions.	Thrust taken by a disc pressing on a rubber sac – communicated hydraulically by small-bore metal tubes to pressure gauge on the test panel in the control room.
Intakes positioned in line with each test cell at the front of the building.		

APPENDIX D

SKETCH AND PLAN OF THE TYPE I TEST-HOUSE AT WATERLOO MILL – BASED ON THE ARRANGEMENT IMMEDIATELY BEFORE DEMOLITION (circa 1989)

This brick-built structure with concrete roof and lintels was situated in the mill yard of the Waterloo Mill. It was the first of the three engine testbeds subsequently built on the site being constructed and put into operation during 1941.

KEY :-

1. Main entrance – access to control/observation room and to twin test cells. Engines for test were positioned in the test cells using a lifting block which moved on an overhead runway located just inside the entrance.

2/3. Rearward facing air-intake towers.

4. Control/observation room serving both engine test cells with roof-mounted ventilation chimneys. Two observation windows overlooked each test chamber.

5/6. Twin engine test cells housing test beds numbered 1 & 2.

7. Blocked window aperture – this feature was incorporated into the building when it was used for other purposes in the post-war period.

8/9. Bricked-up sections of outer test-cell wall indicating the positions of the side air intakes which were deleted in 1942.

10/11. Low apertures with internal sliding doors. The jetpipes of engines on test protruded through these openings and were shielded externally by blackout hoods which allowed night operations to take place.

12. Outer walled compound surrounding the jet exhaust area. A sloping metal deflector plate was originally sited in line with each of the two jet exhausts to deflect the airstream through 90 degrees.

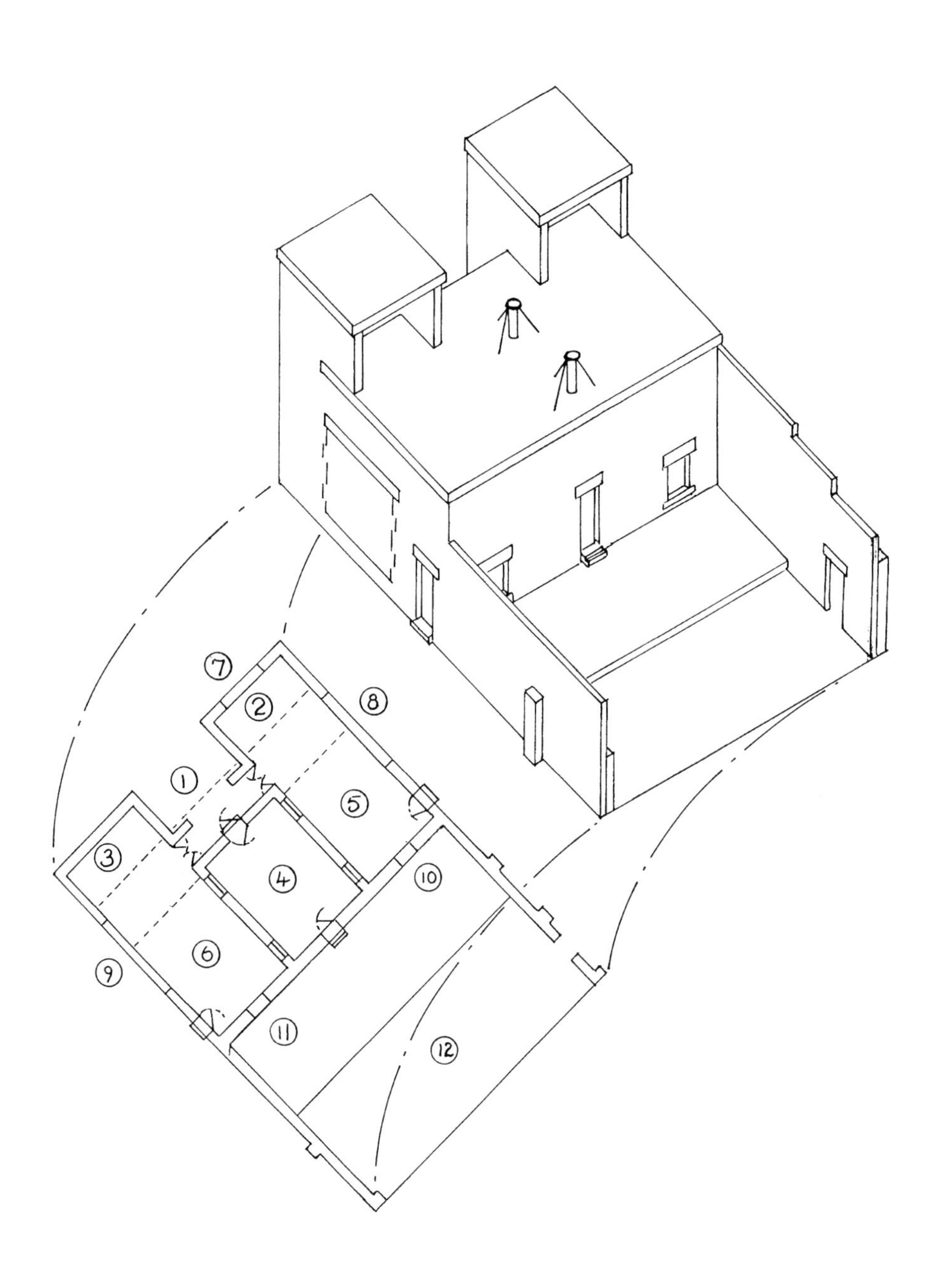
7
2
8
1
5
3
4
10
6
9
11
12

APPENDIX D

A PLAN SHOWING THE TYPE III ENGINE TEST-HOUSE (built 1943-44)

Like the two earlier test-house structures at Waterloo Mill, this building was brick-built with concrete roof and lintels. The exhaust gases were discharged through the wall apertures in a south-easterly direction over the Mearley Brook.

KEY :-

1. Entrance bay to test beds number 5 and number 6 and to their centrally-positioned control room.

2. Entrance bay to test beds number 7 and number 8 and to their centrally-positioned control room.

3/4. Control rooms.
The main observation window was sited to give adequate vision to the operator. An additional window was positioned to one side of this for viewing the front of the engine and another window was provided in the rear corner of the room for observing the jet discharge.

5. Test bed number 5.

6. Test bed number 6.

7. Test bed number 7.

8. Test bed number 8.

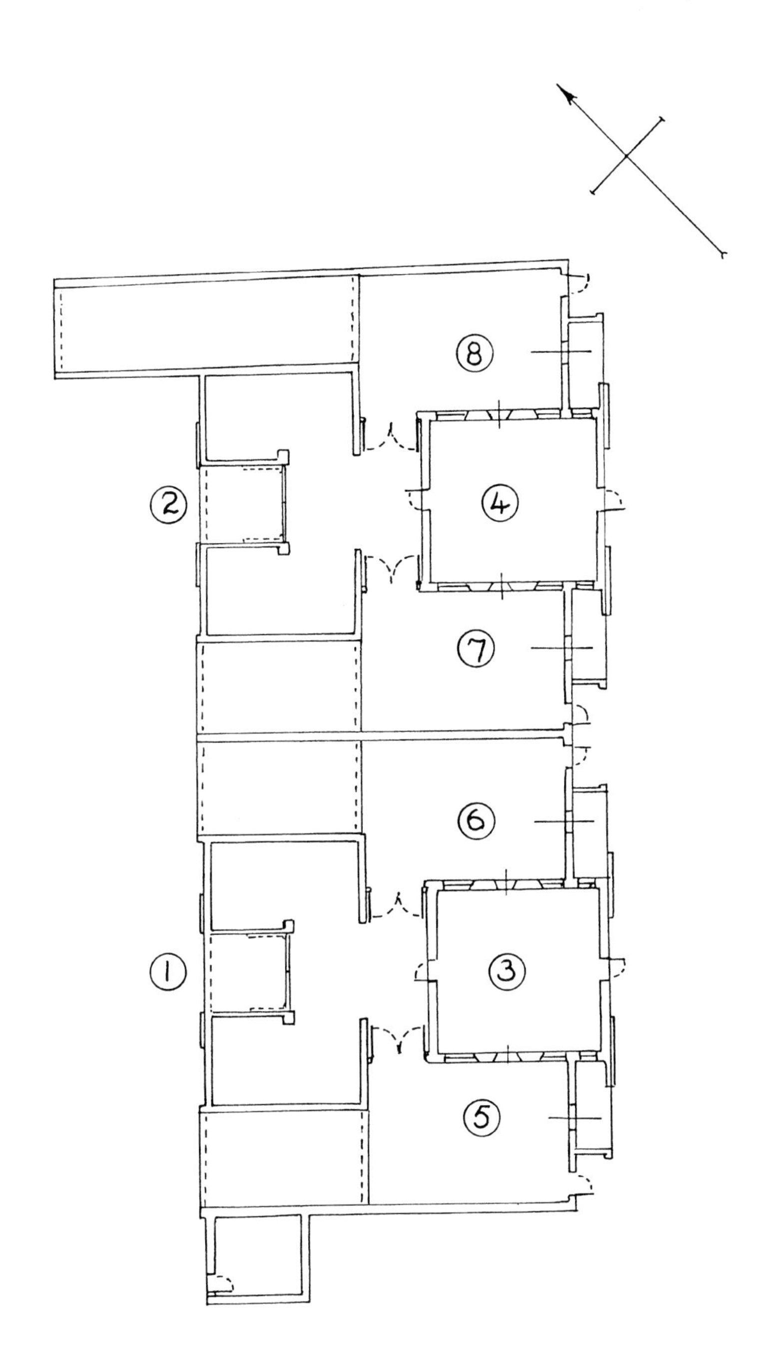

8
2
4
7
6
1
3
5

APPENDIX E

THE ROVER-DESIGNED W2B/26 STRAIGHT-FLOW ENGINE

The design of this new engine arrangement was begun in mid 1941 and within nine months or so a prototype engine, designated STX, was on test, being run for the first time at Waterloo Mill in early March 1942.

Subsequent development engines were given designations with numeric suffixes by the Rover Company (eg ST1, ST2 etc). By the date of the official exchange between Rover and Rolls-Royce, at the beginning of April 1943, three of these later development engines were on test and others were in various stages of construction at Barnoldswick.

The Rover-designed W2B/26 straight-flow engine.

Engine Design Details :-

Compressor – Rover-designed blower case with 20-vane diffuser. Single-stage, double-entry, centrifugal compressor with double-sided impeller.
Combustion Chambers – Ten straight-through flow combustion chambers with colander-ended, stubless flame tubes.
Turbine – Single-stage, axial flow, 80-bladed turbine. Blades with a 5 degree skew were introduced on unit ST3.
Mounting – Two trunions mounted on the horizontal centre-line of the compressor casing together with a torsionally-free diamond frame with link connections and two pick-up points at the rear position.
Bearings on rotor assembly – Plain bearings throughout: front and rear journal only, centre journal and double Michell.

Performance :-

The following ratings were established for the 50-hour Endurance Test with unit ST1, completed in February 1943:-

Take-off rating – 1488 lb thrust at 16500 rpm.
Cruising rating – 1295 lb thrust at 15800 rpm.

Testing established:-

Fuel Consumption – at 1500 lb thrust – 1770 lb/hr.
and at 1300 lb thrust – 1550 lb/hr.
Highest recorded thrust during 50-hour test – 1607 lb.

Preliminary tests for 100 hour type approval test at 1600 lb thrust carried out on unit ST3 in May 1943 established the following ratings :-

Maximum take off – 1600 lb thrust at 16800 rpm.
All out level and combat climbing – 1450 lb thrust at 16400 rpm.
Maximum cruising condition – 1250 lb thrust at 15800 rpm.

The B26 units STX to ST4

STX – The proof of concept/prototype engine. This unit had completed 33 hours 43 minutes running time from its first run in March 1942 to November of the same year. The engine was shown as 'Stripped' on all subsequent monthly reports through to April 1943.

ST1 – First built in October 1942 and put on test in the following month. On first build this unit incorporated the actual STX combustion units complete with STX jets. Correct ST combustion equipment was installed, as it became available, for test ST1/5.

Mock-up. A mock-up of the engine was constructed and despatched to Gloster Aircraft in December 1942 to enable the necessary modifications to be made in the rear spars of the F9/40 aircraft's wing. The mock-up engine was constructed mainly using scrap and wooden components with fuel system and lubrication pipework added and incorporating the proposed form of rear engine mounting.

ST2 – First tested in January 1943 this unit had completed almost 94 hours running time by the end of March 1943.

ST3 – First run in March 1943 when preliminary running-in tests were conducted.

In April 1943 this unit had to be rebuilt following damage caused by the breaking away of a 'jet body' on test. The turbine from ST4, with blades set at a skew of +5 degrees, was fitted in the rebuild. During May 1943 a 100-hour test was commenced with this unit at a static thrust of 1600 lb.

The month-end report for May 1943 stated that this unit would be the last engine to attempt type or endurance running at Waterloo Mill and that in future these tests would all be carried out at Barnoldswick.

ST4 – This unit, which was also referred to by Rolls-Royce as 'B26 No 4' and 'B26 4', was utilised for various tests by Rolls-Royce and was photographed on the testbeds in early 1945.

* * * * *

B37 No 1 – Completed 6 hours 47 minutes running in time on the test beds in June 1943 with Rolls-Royce

APPENDIX F

THE ROVER COMPANY'S ENGINE TESTING UP TO 31 MAY 1942

Engine Unit	① B5101106 (SR102) built 11/41(?)		③ B5121108 (SR104) built 12/41		B51012109 (SR105) built 1/42	
Periods covered by reports	Engine running		Engine running		Engine running	
	During period	Accumltd time	During period	Accumltd time	During period	Accumltd time
Before 3 Dec/41 (*)	2h-01m	2h-01m	–	–	–	–
3 Dec/41-12 Jan/42	**16h-34m**	18h-35m	**1h-17m**	**1h-17m**	–	–
12 Jan/42- 4 Feb/42	**0h-20m**	**18h-55m**	3h-45m	**5h-02m**	–	–
5 Feb/42- 7 Apr/42 (*)	3h-15m	**22h-10m**	12h-19m	**17h-21m**	?	?
8 Apr/42-31 May/42	**16h-30m**	**38h-40m**	**7h-44m**	**25h-05m**	?	**8h-09m**
	[Taxying Engine for F9/40. Despatched 30/5/42]				[Flight Engine for Wellington Test-bed. Despatched 16/7/42]	

Notes:

The system of identifying individual engine units up to June 1942 consisted of a 7-digit reference number with the prefix 'B' (8-digits being used in the case of the B26/ST). The general code appears to have been as follows:-

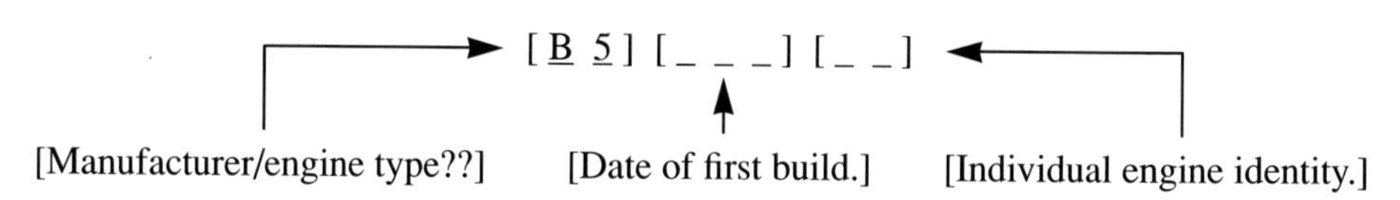

From mid-1942 this system was replaced by a new system of reference whereby all W2B units were identified by the prefix 'SR' (Supercharger-Rover??), together with a 3-digit serial, the retrospective series commencing with SR101. (For a brief period in June/July 1942 W2B identities were recorded as SR1, SR2 etc). The prototype B26 (or ST) engine was referred to as STX with subsequent units being numbered in the series ST1, ST2 etc.

B5022110 (SR106) built 2/42		B5032111 (SR107) built 3/42		(SR108) (SR109)#	B5042114 (SR110) built 4/42		B26032101 (STX) built 3/42		TOTAL RUNNING TIMES DURING EACH OF THE PERIODS
Engine running		Engine running			Engine running		Engine running		
During period	Accumltd time	During period	Accumltd time		During period	Accumltd time	During period	Accumltd time	
–	–	–	–		–	–	–	–	2h-01m
–	–	–	–		–	–	–	–	**17h-51m**(†)
–	–	–	–		–	–	–	–	**4h-05m**
11h-53m	**11h-53m**	8h-42m	**8h-42m**		?	?	?	?	?
35h-00m	**46h-53m**	**15h-00m**	**23h-42m**		?	**1h-50m**	?	**6h-51m**	**96h-37m**(?)
		[Taxying engine for F9/40. Despatched 8/6/42]		(X)	[Low initial performance. Later used as the flight engine for E28/39. Despatched 1/43.]		[Prototype/Proof of Concept Straight-Through engine. First tested 7/3/42]		

The Rover Company received a direct Air Ministry contract for the construction of the experimental W2 engines together with an additional contract to cover testing. The running times for these W2 units have not been included in this table [but see (†) below].

Running times in **heavy type** are as recorded in the various progress reports. Other times have been calculated, where possible, from these figures.

(*) Reports have not been located for these periods.

① & ③ The first and third W2B units were despatched to Power Jets for testing.

(†) An additional 1h-17m running time was recorded for the period 3 Dec/41-12 Jan/42 using a W2 engine for the purpose of 'Proof Testing the new Test House'.

[X] W2B unit SR108 ran at Waterloo Mill for the first time in June but was wrecked on 24/6/42 due to a burst impeller.

(#) W2B unit SR109 seems to have been despatched for tests elsewhere.

APPENDIX F

ENGINE TESTING FROM MID-1942 TO 31 MAY 1943(*)

A) Running-times for the two types of engine on test at Waterloo and Bankfield during this period.

Month	W2B running during month	B26 running during month	Total engine running-time during month	Accumulated running-time to month end (#)
1942	h-m	h-m	h-m	h-m
Jun	13-31	9-22	22-53	-
Jul	29-46	2-01	31-47	212-37
Aug	61-49	3-14	65-03	280-39
Sept	55-26	1-40	57-06	345-09
Oct	88-06	7-49	95-55	429-45
Nov	85-48	10-19	96-07	537-25
Dec	258-17	14-40	272-57	814-02
1943				
Jan	261-27	134-36	396-03	1210-11
Feb	240-19	126-36	366-55	1582-06
Mar	297-34	43-42	341-16	1928-16
	X—	———	———	—X
Apr	170-15	42-11	212-26	2140-42
May	207-23	59-24	266-47	2407-29

Notes:-

* The data for these tables was taken from the internal monthly reports which formed the basis for periodic company reports to the Gas Turbine Collaboration Committee.

\# Figures for Accumulated running time in table A include taxying and flight-test times. These elements are not included in the monthly engine running times for tests on site at Clitheroe and Barnoldswick – hence one reason for the apparent discrepancies between these two sets of figures.

X—X April 1st 1943 marks the official date for the exchange of facilities between the Rover and Rolls-Royce companies.

B) Running-times for each of the B26/ST units.

Engine unit	STX		ST1		ST2		ST3	
	Running -time during month	Total to month end	Running -time during month	Total to month end	Running -time during month	Total to month end	Running -time during month	Total to month end
Month 1942	h-m	h-m	h-m	h-m	h-m	h-m	h-m	h-m
Jun	9-22	16-13						
Jul	2-01	18-14						
Aug	3-14	21-28						
Sept	1-40	23-08						
Oct	7-49	30-57						
Nov	2-46	33-43	7-33	7-33				
Dec	0-00	33-43	14-40?	23-15				
1943								
Jan	0-00	33-43	95-05	118-20	39-31	39-31		
Feb	0-00	33-43	107-20	225-40	19-16	58-47		
Mar	0-00	33-43	3-24	229-04	35-03	93-50	5-15	5-15
	X————	————	————	————	————	————	————	————X
Apr					9-58		32-13	
May			0-35				58-49	96-17

C) Engine testing at Clitheroe and Barnoldswick.
[These monthly statistics are the only ones found which show a break down of the running-times at the two test sites].

Month	Clitheroe During month	Clitheroe Accumulated running-time	Barnoldswick During month	Barnoldswick Accumulated running-time
1942	h-m	h-m	h-m	h-m
Jul	28-28	200-04	3-19	12-33
Aug	16-50	225-11	42-55	55-28
Sept	46-53	279-28	10-13	65-41
Oct	85-11	366-11	10-44	63-34 ??
Nov	62-40	428-51	32-27	108-34

[Note – the error in the figure originally recorded for October's accumulated running-time at Barnoldswick would appear to explain the error in accumulated running time for October in table A.]

BIBLIOGRAPHY

PUBLISHED BOOKS

Gas Turbines and Jet Propulsion, by G Geoffrey Smith,
Revised & Enlarged by F C Sheffield, published by Iliffe & Sons Ltd.
(First published 1942 – sixth edition 1955)
Jet Flight, by John Grierson,
published by Sampson Low, Marston & Co Ltd. (1945)
Jane's all the World's Aircraft 1945-46, by Leonard Bridgeman,
published by Sampson Low, Marston & Co Ltd. (1946)
Jet – The Story of a Pioneer, by Sir Frank Whittle, KCB, CB, FRS,
published by Frederick Muller Ltd. (1953)
History of the Second World War – Design and Development of Weapons
Studies in Government and Industrial Organisation, by M M Postan,
D Hay and J D Scott,
published by HMSO & Longmans. (1964)
The Rover Story, by Graham Robson,
published by Patrick Stephens. (1977)
Lucas – The First Hundred Years, (2 vols) by Harold Nockolds,
published by David & Charles. (1978)
Rolls-Royce – The Merlin at War, by Ian Lloyd,
published by The Macmillan Press Ltd. (1978)
Churches, Canals & Pubs, some drawings by Henson Bamford,
published Privately. (1981)
Not Much of an Engineer, by Sir Stanley Hooker,
published by Airlife. (1984)
Rolls-Royce – Hives, the Quiet Tiger, by A Harvey Bailey,
published by Rolls-Royce Heritage Trust. (1985)
Gloster Aircraft Since 1917, by Derek N James,
published by Putnam. (1987) (second ed.)
Whittle – The True Story, by John Golley,
published by Airlife. (1987)
The Jet Pioneers, by Glyn Jones,
published by Methuen. (1989)
Lucas at War – A souvenir brochure to commemorate the 50th anniversary
of the Battle of Britain,
published by Lucas Aerospace. (1990)
Industrial Heritage – A Guide to the Industrial Archaeology of the
Ribble Valley, by Mike Rothwell,
published by Bridgestone Press. (1990)

Rolls-Royce – Hives' Turbulent Barons by Alec Harvey-Bailey, published by Rolls-Royce Heritage Trust. (1992)
Rover the First Ninety Years by Eric Dymock, published by Dove Publishing. (1993)

UNPUBLISHED MATERIAL

Business Records of the Rover Co Ltd. (BMIHT)
Reports of the Rover Company for monthly submissions to the Gas Turbine Collaboration Committee. (1941-43)
Development and Research Work Carried out on W2B Superchargers. (1942)
ST1 Report. (1943)
Turbo Jet Test Houses at Waterloo Mill. (n d)
Gas Turbine Development, by J Watt – Lucas. (1947)
The Rover Company and the Gas Turbine for Automobile Propulsion by H B Light. (1965)
A Brief History of Lucas in Burnley, by Roy O Windley, Lucas. (1980) (Issue 2)
Archival records of the Rolls-Royce Heritage Trust.
Miscellaneous papers, correspondence, etc.

Borough of Clitheroe – Council Minutes.
Barnoldswick UDC – Council Minutes.

JOURNALS, MAGAZINE & NEWSPAPER ARTICLES.

The Early History of the Whittle Jet Propulsion Gas Turbine, by Air Commodore F Whittle. The First James Clayton Lecture, Journal of the Institution Of Mechanical Engineers. (1946)
The Journal of the Royal Aeronautical Society.
'The Archive' – Journal of the Rolls-Royce Heritage Trust.

Twentyfirst Profile – Volume 1 No 8. A New Concept of Flight (The Gloster Whittle E28/39).
Twentyfirst Profile – Volume 2 No 14. (1991) The F9/40 Prototypes.
The Clitheroe Advertiser and Times.
The Clitheroe Borough Record.
The Manchester Guardian.

ACKNOWLEDGEMENTS

The compilation of this study would not have been possible without the help given by a great number of individuals. I owe particular debt of gratitude to the many current and past employees of the Rover, Lucas and Rolls-Royce Companies, and others, who have been bombarded with my abstruse questions and who have dug deep into their memories to provide answers. They are :- Mr Max Alderson, Mr Jack Altham, Mr David Ballantyne, Mr Joe Bamford, Mr Tom Barton, Mrs Florence Bennett, Mr John Bennett, Mr Wilf Bennett, Mr C Berry, Mr Jim Boal, Mrs Gladys Booth, Mr Charles Bottoms, Mrs Annie Broom, Mrs Millicent Bunn, Mrs Kathleen Butler, Mr Bill Cavill, Mr K Chippendale, Mr Roy Clough, Mrs Gillian Creed, Miss Marie Cullen, Mr Doug Daniels, Mr Joe Drinkwater, Mr Harold Duckworth, Mr Eric Edmondson, Mr Frank Foreman, Mr John Gardiner, Mr & Mrs Geoff Fox, Mr Jack Gregory, Mr Ken Hall, Mrs Betty Hargreaves, Mr Wilf Heatley, Mr Les Holliday, Mr Bert Jones, Mr Jack Kenyon, Mr Don Lawson, Mrs Jenny Limbert, Mrs Mary Miller, Mr Arthur Neal, Mr Allan Oddie, Mr Harry Pearson, Mr John Price, Mr Ken Ranson, Mr Les Saye, Mrs Connie Seagar, Mr Richard Sharples, Mr Kelvin Shew, Mrs Jean Shuttleworth, Mr A Bernard Smith, Mrs N Snape, Mr John Swaine, Mr David Taylor, Mr John Taylor, Mr Harry Teggardine, Mr Bill Tremble, Mrs Madge Vose, Mr John Weightman, Mr Ernie West, Mrs Margaret Wigglesworth, Mr Stan Wilkinson, Mr Gordon Wood and Mr Harold Yates.

I gratefully acknowledge the invaluable assistance given to me by those who have enabled me to study contemporary records or have provided other information or materials. Special appreciation is expressed to – Mr Ron Driver, Mr Mike Evans and Mr Richard Haigh of Rolls-Royce plc; Mr Kenyon R Owens of Inco Alloys Ltd; Mr Richard A Storey of the Modern Records Centre, University of Warwick Library; Mr Ken Haworth of the North West Sound Archives; Mr Ian Potter of the Ribble Valley Council; Mr Cyril Ainsworth; Mrs Joan Lombard; Mr A B Smith; Mr John Swaine and Mr Roy Windley.

I would particularly like to thank Mrs Elizabeth King and Mrs Avril Moore for their permission to reproduce the sketch of Waterloo Mill drawn by their late father – Mr J Henson Bamford.

My thanks also go to the staff of the Local Studies Section of the Clitheroe and Barnoldswick Libraries, and of the City of Coventry Central Library; Mr Maurice Dunphy; Mr John Barry and Mr Peter Devine of the Clitheroe Advertiser & Times; and to Mr David Birch of the Rolls-Royce Heritage Trust.

PHOTOGRAPHIC AND OTHER CREDITS

Acknowledgements and thanks are due to the following sources who have kindly made available the illustrations used in this book:-

Mrs Greta Barker; Barnoldswick Local History Group, via the Lancashire Library; Mr John Bennett; Mr Chaz Bowyer; Mr Jack Gregory; Rolls-Royce plc – via Mrs Joan Lombard; Lucas Heritage Trust; Mrs Mary Miller; Mr Allan Oddie; Mr J C Pye; Mr Graham Robson; all uncredited photographs copyright Rolls-Royce plc.

Acknowledgement is also given for the following :-

The illustration of the Viking warrior on the title page is taken from a Rover Company advertisement, circa 1928.
The map reproduced as illustration on page 19 is taken from the 1931 edition of Ordnance Survey map sheet XLVII 10 in the 1:2500 series.
The photographs of the Type I test-house (pages 34, 35 and 36) and the Lucas drawing of the Combustion Chamber Dome Assembly (page 39) are taken from the report entitled – 'Development And Research Work Carried out on W2B Superchargers During the Period April – May 1942', prepared by the Rover Company.
Sir Wilfrid Freeman's letter to Spencer Wilks (page 69) is taken from the Rover Board Minutes, held for the British Motor Industries Heritage Trust at the University of Warwick.
The advertisement celebrating a 'New World Record' (page 80) is taken from the edition of 'The Aeroplane' magazine dated January 4, 1946.
The comments of test-pilot John Grierson, quoted on pages 98 and 99, are taken from his book 'Jet Flight', published by Sampson Low, Marston & Co, Ltd, in 1945.

The remaining illustrations are from the Author's collection.

If any person or body should feel that they have been overlooked or inadequately thanked, I would like them to know that this will be through ignorance or inadvertence and not through design. I ask them to accept my sincere apologies.

RR
ROLLS-ROYCE
HERITAGE TRUST